National Key Scl

Accessible Toilets for Disa

Published by RADAR PROMOTIONS LTD for

Registered Charity Number 273150

THE ROYAL ASSOCIATION FOR DISABILITY RIGHTS

12 City Forum
250 City Road
London EC1V 8AF

Tel: 020 7250 3222
Fax: 020 7250 0212
Minicom 020 7250 4119
www.radar.org.uk

Compliled by
John Stanford

ISBN 978-0-9561995-5-3
12th Edition © RADAR PROMOTIONS LTD 2010

Contents

Publisher
Adrian Chance
adrian.chance@radar.org.uk

Sales & Production coordinator
marriott.lusengo@radar.org.uk
Marriott Lusengo

Design
Marriot Lusengo
marriott.lusengo@radar.org.uk

Printed by
Cambrian Printers
Lianbadarn Road
Aberystwyth Dyfed SY23
www.cambrian-printers.co.uk
01970 627 111

Contents

❯ RADAR believes that everyone who experiences ill-health, injury or disability should have the same freedom and independence as other citizens. We need changes in our society to achieve that – from better independent living and social care support to routes out of poverty – and RADAR is campaigning on all those issues, working in Parliament, with policy makers and with many other organisations to achieve change. We produce booklets, written by and for disabled people, on subjects from employment and managing money to making the most of information technology.

RADAR (Royal Association for Disability Rights) is led by people with direct personal experience of disability or health conditions. We have over 400 organisational members. We support disabled people's leadership and empowerment: for instance, in 2010 we are supporting 100 disabled people to pursue their leadership ambitions and make a difference, influencing planning, education, health, social care and more.

In the last year we have made important national policy gains. We influenced Government to improve the Access to Work scheme (increasing the budget and making it better for people with fluctuating conditions). We influenced the Equality Bill, to make sure nothing was lost from the Disability Discrimination Act and that there were new rights: no pre-employment health checks before job offer (to rule out unfair job discrimination); and new rights for disabled children to auxiliary aids at school.

One important part of freedom is having the confidence to go out, knowing that public toilets will be available that are accessible and meet your requirements. This guide, which includes information on Changing Places toilets, provides all you need to know about the National Key Scheme and the accessible toilets around the country.

For more information about all our work go to 🅦 www.radar.org.uk

❯ **Liz Sayce OBE**, Chief Executive
March 2010

Introduction

●   For people living with ill-health, injury or disability to be able to engage in their communities and take part in everyday activities, the availability of appropriately designed lavatories in public places is essential. This can make the difference between having the confidence to go out and enjoy activities – or having to stay at home. Ideally RADAR would like accessible public toilets to be open and kept in a usable condition at all times. However, toilets can become unusable by disabled people even if there is only a low level of damage or lack of maintenance. Unfortunately, in many situations the providers have found it necessary to restrict entry to purpose designed toilets in order to prevent damage caused either wilfully or by more casual misuse. Therefore RADAR, in discussion with disability organisations, local authorities and others established the National Key Scheme for Toilets for Disabled People. It has proved very popular.

With the National Key Scheme, a standard lock can be fitted if the local authority or other provider, in discussion with disabled people, considers it necessary to lock toilets for disabled people separately from others. Local Authorities adopting the scheme should make arrangements for disabled people in their area to obtain a key. Wherever possible a key should be held near each toilet that is fitted with the NKS lock. Disabled people can also acquire a key from RADAR, who also undertake to keep a list of toilets fitted with the NKS lock. The National Key Scheme was launched nearly 30 years ago and many disabled people tell us they value it highly for the increased independence it provides – both by reducing damage and misuse and by cutting out the need to ask for staff to unlock a toilet.

This current listing includes over 8000 toilets in all parts of the country. These are provided by almost all local authorities that have public toilets and an increasingly wide range of other organisations. While some Councils have closed a number of their public conveniences for disabled people or transferred them to other bodies, a larger number have continued to expand their provision, at least modestly. The NKS has been integral in the development of automatic, vandal resistant "superloos" that can be used by disabled people. The scheme has become a normal part of provision in most parts of the country. More recently the Changing Places campaign has pioneered the opening of toilets incorporating adult changing facilities (see below). RADAR is very supportive of this development and has included Changing Places toilets in the Guide.

Changing Places Toilets

Some disabled people need facilities beyond those found in a "standard" toilet designed for disabled people. Changing Places toilets have;

- An adjustable height adult changing table
- A hoist either with tracking or mobile
- Space both sides of the WC for assistants.

Changing Places toilets around the country are listed in this guide and shown by (CP). As yet there are very few of these and most are only available when the premises in which they are situated are open. The entries for those that are not fitted with the NKS lock are shown in brackets. For further information about Changing Places call;

☎ 020 7696 6019 or in Scotland ☎ 01382 385154

or see ⬜ www.changing-places.org

The National Key Scheme has never been confined to local authority public conveniences – from its early days the lock was fitted at railway stations and some National Trust properties. Over recent years private organisations have been a major area of growth in the scheme and toilets fitted with the NKS lock can now be found in shopping centres, pubs, cafes, department stores, motorway service areas and many other locations around the country. As the number of toilets fitted with the standard lock has grown, so has the proportion of disabled people who have a NKS key. RADAR has regularly referred to the scheme in its own publications and has sought other publicity. At a local level some authorities have successfully and imaginatively publicised the scheme while elsewhere information and consultation have been less than adequate. Local disability organisations have often played a major role in informing disabled people about the scheme and, in some cases, in persuading local authorities and other organisations to take part.

❯ The non-toilet use of the NKS

From the early stages of the development of the scheme, owners of a number of types of premises saw that it could be used in situations other than public toilets. An accessible entrance to a building may not be permanently open for security reasons. In rural areas it may be necessary to prevent stock straying or horses or motorcycles from damaging footpaths. The National Trust and other conservation bodies have properties at which only cars containing disabled people are allowed into certain areas. The use of the National Key Scheme is one way in which access can be made possible for disabled people in such situations either using a regular mortise lock or a NKS padlock that is also available. The current design recommendations for a unisex public toilet have focused on the features that are required for wheelchair users and people who can walk only a short distance.

❯ The design and use of toilets for disabled people

The approach must be level or ramped, the doorway level and of an adequate width and the dimensions large enough for wheelchair manoeuvre to allow for different directions of transfer to the WC and for personal assistance if this is required. The fact that some disabled people will need assistance from a companion necessitates a unisex cubicle. The recommended layout of fittings aims to cater for the maximum possible range of requirements.

As the scheme has grown, it has became clear that people with a far wider range of experiences of ill-health or disability required certain aspects of specially designed toilets and the means of entry to them. For many the unisex nature of the facilities is necessary. For example, people with Alzheimer's who might otherwise require their clothing to be adjusted in the street by a companion. Some blind people welcome being able to avoid the threatening atmosphere of too many public conveniences and the space that can be used by a guide dog. Speedy access to a toilet can be necessary for some with bladder conditions. People with a range of conditions need a wash basin close to the WC and the generally more hygienic conditions that they can expect to find in a toilet fitted with the NKS lock.

The provision of well-designed public unisex toilets designed for disabled people does not mean there is no need to pay attention to the design and maintenance of other toilets. Simple fittings such as a handrail in at least one WC cubicle and by a urinal would help a large number of people. Some trends such as reduced size of cubicles and of the height of WCs are actually making modern public toilets more difficult, or even impossible, for many people to use.

Finally, local authorities and other providers of public toilets provided most of the information in this book. This was supported by material from individual users, local access guides and other sources. I would like to thank everyone involved for their assistance and our advertisers for their support. All information is provided in good faith but RADAR cannot be held responsible for any omissions or inaccuracies. We would be pleased to hear of any additions or amendments that may be required for future editions.

John Stanford, Editor
March 2010

❯ The toilets listed in this publication are those that we have been told are fitted with the National Key Scheme lock - it is not a list of all public toilets designed for disabled people in the country. Indeed although we have tried to contact all organisations who are likely to provide NKS toilets there may be some of which we have no information or which have not responded.

❯ **Information in entries**

In general the entries in this guide are of unisex toilets designed for disabled people that are available to NKS keyholders at all times. Providers were asked to specify those that did not comply with this.

Toilets that are not unisex are indicated in this guide by the **M** and **F** symbols.

Some toilets are not available at all times; they may be within premises that are closed overnight or entire blocks may be closed down on a seasonal basis. Where this applies an indication of the opening times is shown in the entry, e.g. (08.00-20.00), (Summer) or (Park hrs). It should also be assumed that most of the non-District Council toilets (see below) would not be available on a 24-hour basis.

A number of entries are for toilets that, at the time of writing, have not yet been opened although plans to do so are firm. In a smaller number of cases there are plans to replace or close the toilets at particular locations at some time in the future. These are indicated by, for example (Summer 10), (Proposed) or (to be replaced).

❯ **Non-District Council toilets**

Most toilets fitted with the NKS lock are run by the District or Borough Council in whose area they are located. However an increasing number are now provided by other organisations. These include other public authorities such as Parish and County Councils, commercial bodies including shopping centres, public houses and rail companies and a wide variety of other public and voluntary organisations.

An indication of the ownership of these non-District Council toilets is given at the end of the entry, e.g. [National Trust], [ScotRail] or [Nando's]. Some of these designations have been abbreviated, e.g.

[JDW] for J D Wetherspoon pubs, [NP] for National Park and [GMPTE] for Greater Manchester Passenger Transport Executive.
In other instances [Private] has been used. Although some of these toilets can be considered and used as ordinary public conveniences, in most cases they are provided essentially for the customers or users of the premises and not available, as of right, to the public. They will also only usually be available when the premises are open.
 Order of Entries
The entries are listed in Regions and then by Local Authority area. The Regions and the areas they represent are as follows:

---

1 ❯ Greater London
A Central London area, roughly that within the ring of Railway Terminals, includes the City of London and parts of Camden, Islington, Lambeth, Southwark and Westminster. Outside this area entries are listed under Borough headings.

---

2 ❯ South East England
East Sussex, Kent, Surrey and West Sussex.

---

3 ❯ Southern England
Berkshire, Buckinghamshire, Hampshire, the Isle of Wight, Oxfordshire and the south eastern part of Dorset, including Bournemouth and Poole.

---

4 ❯ West Country
Gloucestershire, Somerset, Wiltshire, most of Dorset and the area around Bristol.

---

5 ❯ Devon & Cornwall.

---

7 ❯ East Anglia
Bedfordshire, Cambridgeshire, Essex, Hertfordshire, Norfolk and Suffolk.

---

8 ❯ East Midlands
Derbyshire, Leicestershire, Lincolnshire, Northamptonshire and Nottinghamshire and the southern part of the area that used to form Humberside.

---

9 ❯ West Midlands
Herefordshire, Shropshire, Staffordshire, Warwickshire, West Mid lands and Worcestershire.

How to use this guide

Within Regions, Local Authority districts are listed alphabetically. Within districts, localities such as towns and villages are listed, again in alphabetic order. In each locality the locations of individual toilets are given, although in some rural areas specific locations are not available. Those toilets provided by the relevant Council are given first, followed by any provided by other organisations (see above). Changing Places toilets are indicated by the CP logo. The entries for those for which the NKS key is not required are in brackets.

To assist in finding entries, particularly when travelling away from your home area, an index of localities is given at the back of the book, see page 322. This includes all towns and villages but not all the localities of big towns and cities that are included in the main listings. For example Manchester is listed in the index but not the 14 individual areas of the city that are found on pages 208 - 223.

Natural England is an independent public body whose purpose is to protect and improve England's natural environment and encourage people to enjoy and get involved in their surroundings. We promote access, recreation and well-being and ensure natural resources are managed so they can be enjoyed now and by future generations.

In all our work we strive to ensure that the natural world is accessible to all and are committed to establishing a diverse and inclusive workforce. Your ability is what we are interested in, whether you want to apply for advertised roles or to volunteer your time and skills as part of our extensive volunteering programme. Our roles are as diverse as our people - from communications experts, environmental scientists, bat workers, business managers, to IT specialists. We welcome applications from people with disabilities and recruit through fair and open competition to all our posts.

If you think your skills could help Natural England conserve the natural environment, find out more from our website at www.naturalengland.org.uk.

CENTRAL LONDON

E1 ❯
Spitalfields Market (Trading hrs) (Private)
Nandos, Middlesex Street (Nandos)
Nandos, 114 Commercial Street (Nandos)
Shooting Star, Middlesex Street (Fullers)
Slug & Lettuce, Stoney Lane (Private)

EC1 ❯
City Road/Central Street (Islington)
Clerkenwell Road/Leather Lane (Camden)
Long Lane, Aldersgate St (City of London)
West Smithfield (City of London)
Finsbury Leisure Centre (Centre hrs) (Islington)
Bar 38, St Johns Street (Private)
Butchers Hook & Cleaver, Smithfield (Fullers)
Lord Raglan, St Martin-Le-Grand (Private)
Printworks, Farringdon Road (JDW)
Sir John Oldcastle, Farringdon Road (JDW)
Three Compasses, Cowcross Street (Private)

EC2 ❯
Liverpool St Station, Platform 10 (Network Rail)
Bishopsgate Institute (Centre hrs) (Private)
All Bar One, Finsbury Pavement (M&B)

Caffe Nero, London Wall (Private)
Green Man, Poultry (JDW)
Hamilton Hall, Liverpool St. Station (JDW)
Rack & Tenter, Moorfields (Private)
The Wren, Liverpool St Station (Private)
Guildhall School of Music (Concert hrs) (Private)

EC3 ❯
Monument (City of London)
Tower Place (City of London)
Fenchurch Street Station, Lower Level
(Network Rail)
All Bar One, Houndsditch (M&B)
Bar 38, St Clare House, Minories (Private)
Caffe Nero, London St, Fenchurch St (Private)
Crosse Keys, Gracechurch Street (JDW)
Fine Line Monument Street (Fullers)
Liberty Bounds, Trinity Square (JDW)
Slug & Lettuce, St Mary Axe (Private)

EC4 ❯
New Change, St Paul's Churchyard (City of London)

Paternoster Square (Daytime) (City of London)
Blackfriars Station, Concourse (Capital Connect)
Cannon Street Station, Lower Concourse
(Network Rail)
Alibi, Shoe Lane (Private)

All Bar One, Ludgate Hill (M&B)
The Banker, Cousin Lane (Fullers)
Costa, New Bridge Street (Costa)
Fine Line, Bow Churchyard (Fullers)
Hog's Head, Fetter Lane (Private)
Leon, Ludgate Circus (Private)
The Paternoster, Paternoster Square (Private)

N1 ⊗ Kings Cross Station, Platform 8 (Network Rail)

NW1 ⊗ Marylebone Rd, opp. Planetarium (Westminster)
Regents Park (M&F) (4) (Royal Parks)
Marylebone Station, Concourse (Chiltern
Railways)
Globe, Marylebone Road (Private)
Metropolitan Bar, Station Approach (JDW)

SE1 ⊗ Gabriels Wharf (Private)
London Bridge Station, Forecourt & Platforms 5/6
(Network Rail)
Waterloo East Station, Platform B (SE Rlwy)
Waterloo Station, Concourse & Forecourt
(Network Rail)
All Bar One, London Bridge Street (M&B)
Founders Arms, Hopton Street (Youngs)
Market Porter, Stoney Street (Private)
Nandos, Clink Street (Nandos)
City Hall, Queens Walk (Office hrs) (CP)
Tate Modern (Gallery hrs) (CP)

SW1 ⊗ Bressenden Place/Victoria Street (Westminster)
Broad Sanctuary (7.30-23.00) (Westminster)
Tachbrook Street (7.30-23.00) (Westminster)
Westminster Bridge, by Pier (7.30-23.00)
(Westminster)
Victoria Place, Eccleston Bridge (Private)
Victoria Coach Station, Arrivals Area (TfL)
Victoria Coach Station, Help Point (2) (TfL)
Victoria Station (2) (Network Rail

St James's Park, Marlborough Gate (Royal Parks)
Victoria Coach Station, Arrivals Area (TfL)

Victoria Coach Station, Help Point (2) (TfL)
Victoria Station (2) (Network Rail)
St James's Park, Marlborough Gate (Royal Parks)
Cabinet War Rooms (Private)
Ha! Ha! Bar, Cardinal Walk (Private)
Lord Moon of The Mall", Whitehall (JDW)
Nandos, Cardinal Walk (Nandos)
Nandos, 107 Wilton Road (Nandos)
Shakespeare, Buckingham Palace Rd (Private)
Travellers Tavern, Elizabeth Street (Private)
Willow Walk, Wilton Road (JDW)

SW7 ❯ Kensington Rd, opp. Palace Gate (10.00-18.00)
(Westminster)
Mount Gate (M&F) (Royal Parks)

W1 ❯ Balderton St, off Oxford Street (Westminster)
Marble Arch Subway (10.00-23.00) (Westminster)
Paddington St Gardens (Daytime) (Westminster)
Piccadilly Circus Station (Westminster) [Steps on
approach]
Plaza Centre, 1st Floor, Oxford Street (Private)
John Lewis Store, Oxford Street (John Lewis)
Selfridges Store, Oxford Street (Selfridges)
Duke of Wellington, Wardour St (Private)
Nandos, 113 Baker Street (Nandos)
Nandos, Googe Street (Nandos)
O'Neills, Gt Marlborough Street (M&B)
O'Neills, Wardour Street (M&B)
Walkabout, Shaftesbury Ave (Private)

W2 ❯ Paddington Station, Platform 1 (Network Rail)
Hyde Park, Bandstand (Royal Parks)
Hyde Park, Reservoir (Royal Parks)
Garfunkels, Praed Street (Private)
McDonalds, Edgware Road (McDonalds)
Shish, Bishops Bridge Rd (Private)
Tyburn, Edgware Road (JDW)
Grosvenor Victoria Casino, Edgware Rd (Private)

WC1 ❯ High Holborn, opp Proctor Street (Camden)
Russell Square, opp Bernard Street (Camden)
All Bar One, New Oxford Street (M&B)
The Goose, Russell Square (Private)
Nandos, Brunswick Centre (Nandos)

WC1 ❯ High Holborn, opp Proctor Street (Camden)
Russell Square, opp Bernard Street (Camden)
All Bar One, New Oxford Street (M&B)
The Goose, Russell Square (Private)
Nandos, Brunswick Centre (Nandos)
Pendrells Oak, High Holborn (JDW)

WC2 ❯ Embankment, by Underground (7.30-23.00)
(Westminster) (CP)
Jubilee Hall, Covent Garden (7.30-23.00)
(Westminster)
Shaftesbury Avenue, off Piccadilly Circus
(Westminster)
Strand/Arundel Street (Westminster)
Charing Cross Station (Network Rail)
All Bar One, Cambridge Circus (M&B)
All Bar One, Kingsway (M&B)
Brewmaster, Cranbourne St. (Private)
Chiquito, Leicester Square (Private)
Columbia Bar, Aldwych (Private)
Ha! Ha! Bar, Villiers Street (Private)
Knights Templar, Chancery Lane (JDW)
Montagu Pyke, Charing Cross Road (JDW)
Moon Under Water, Leicester Square (JDW)
Nandos, Chandos Place (Nandos)
Shakespeare's Head, Kingsway (JDW)
Walkabout, Henrietta Street (Private)
Walkabout, Temple Place (Private)
Yates's Bar, Leicestevr Square (Yates)
Odeon, Leicester Square (Odeon)
Odeon West End, Leicester Sq (Odeon)
Peacock Theatre, Portugal St (Private)

BARKING & DAGENHAM

Barking ❯ Barking Park, Tennis Courts (8.00-17.00)
Clockhouse Avenue, Town Centre
Faircross
Fanshaw Avenue (Mon-Sat, daytime)
North Street (Mon-Sat, daytime)
Rippleside Cemetery (Mon-Sat, daytime)
Thames View (8.00-17.00)
Vicarage Field Shopping Centre (Private)
Barking Station, Overbridge (C2C)
Barking Dog, Station Parade (JDW)

Nandos, Long Bridge Road (Nandos)

Chadwell Heath ❯ Chadwell Heath Cemetery (Mon-Sat, daytime)
St Chads Park (8.00-17.00)
Coopers Arms, High Road (Private)

Dagenham ❯ Beacontree Heath (8.00-17.00)
Central Park, Pavilion (8.00-17.00)
Eastbrookend Cemetery (Mon-Sat, Daytime)
Heathway/Hedgemans Road
Lodge Avenue
Stamford Road (8.00-17.00)
Dagenham Dock Station, Platform 2 (C2C)
Lord Denman, Heathway (JDW)
Dagenham & Redbridge FC (Private)

BARNET

Childs Hill, NW2 ❯ Childs Hill Park, Nant Road (Park hrs)

Colindale, NW9 ❯ Moon Under Water, Varley Parade (JDW)

East Barnet ❯ Oak Hill Park, Parkside (Park hrs)
Victoria Recreation Ground, Glyn Road (Park hrs)

Edgware ❯ Edgwarebury Park, Edgwarebury Lane (Park hrs)
Nandos, Station Road (Nandos)

Finchley, N3 ❯ Victoria Park, Ballards Lane (Park hrs)

Friern Barnet, N11 ❯ Friary Park, Friern Barnet Road (Park hrs)

Golders Green, N11 ❯ Golders Hill, by Café (City of London)

Hendon, NW4 ❯ Hendon Park, Queens Road (Park hrs)

High Barnet ❯ Old Court House Recreation Ground (Café hrs)

Mill Hill, NW7 ❯ Mill Hill Park, Daws Lane (Park hrs)

New Barnet ❯ Railway Bell, East Barnet Road (JDW)

North Finchley, N12 ❯ Sainsbury's Store, 836-852 High Road
(Sainsbury)
Nandos, Great North Leisure Park (Nandos)

The Tally Ho, 749 High Road (JDW)

Whetstone, N20 ❯ Swan Lane Open Space, café (Café hrs)

BEXLEY

Abbey Wood, SE2 ❯ Lesnes Abbey (Park hrs)
Abbey Wood Station (SE Rlwy)
Abbey Wood Caravan Club Site (Caravan Club)

Albany Park ❯ Albany Park Station (SE Rlwy)

Belvedere ❯ Belvedere Recreation Ground, Heron Hill (Park hrs)
Bexley College, Tower Campus (3) (College)

Bexley ❯ High Street
Bexley Station (SE Rlwy)

Bexleyheath ❯ Danson Park (Park hrs)
Danson Park Mansion (Summer, Park hrs)
Friswell Place
Townley Road
The Mall Bexleyheath (2) (Private)
Bexleyheath Station (SE Rlwy)
Furze Wren, Market Place (JDW)
The Wrong Un, The Broadway (JDW)
Yates's Bar, Mayplace Road West (Yates)
Gala Bingo, Broadway (Gala)

Blackfen ❯ Blackfen Library (Library hrs)

Crayford ❯ Waterside, Crayford Way
Crayford Station (SE Rlwy)
Nandos, Tower Retail Park (Nandos)

Erith ❯ Town Centre

Sidcup ❯ St John's Road
Sidcup Station (SE Rlwy)
Jolly Fenman, Blackfen Road (Private)
Tailors Chalk, Sidcup High Street (JDW)
Woodman, Blackfen Road (Private)

Welling ❯ Hillview Cemetery (Cemetery hrs)
Welling Library, Bellegrove Road (Library hrs)

New Cross Turnpike, Bellegrove Rd (JDW)

BRENT

Alperton	❯	Douglas Avenue/Ealing Road
Brent Cross, NW4	❯	Brent Cross Shopping Centre (Private)
Colindale, NW9	❯	Oriental City Shopping Centre (Private)
Harlesden, NW10	❯	Harlesden Library, Craven Park Rd (Library hrs) Roundwood Park (Park hrs) Tavistock Road Car Park (8.00-17.00) Willesden Junction Station, Platform 1 (London Overground) Misty Moon, Manor Park Road (Private)
Kensal Rise, NW10	❯	Chamberlayne Road/Station Terrace
Kilburn, NW6	❯	Victoria Road/Kilburn High Street Caffe Nero, Kilburn High Road (Private) Nandos, Kilburn High Street (Nandos) Mecca Bingo, Kilburn High Rd (Private) Tricycle Theatre & Cinema, Kilburn High Rd (Private)
Kingsbury, NW9	❯	Kingsbury Road, Car Park JJ Moons, 553 Kingsbury Road (JDW) Nando's, Kingsbury Road (Nandos)
Queens Park, NW6	❯	Car Park by Station Queens Park Café (Park hrs) Queens Park, by Playground (Park hrs)
Sudbury	❯	Barham Park, Car Park
Wembley	❯	Mahatma Ghandi House, Wembley Hill Road (Office hrs) Oakington Manor Drive/Harrow Rd (9.00-19.00) St Johns Road Car Park St Johns Road/Elm Road Church of the Ascension, The Avenue (Church) Paddy Power, 389 High Road (Private) Black Horse, Harrow Road (Private) JJ Moons, 397 High Road (JDW) KFC, 434 High Road (Private) McDonalds,482 High Road (McDonalds)

Nando's, 420 High Road (Nandos)
The Preston, Preston Road (Private)
Wembley Arena (8) (Private)
Wembley Stadium (147) (Private)

Willesden, NW10   ❯   High Road, off Richmond Avenue
Quality House, Willesden Lane (Office hrs)

BROMLEY

Beckenham   ❯   High Street/Kelsey Park Road
Beckenham Junction Station (SE Rlwy)
Clock House Station (SE Rlwy)
Slug & Lettuce, 150 High Street (Private)

Biggin Hill   ❯   Main Road, opp Church Road

Bromley   ❯   The Hill, Beckenham Lane/High Street
Library Gardens, off High Street
Stockwell Building 2, Civic Centre (Office hrs)
Glades MSCP, Level 2 (Private)
Bromley North Station (SE Rlwy)
Bromley South Station, Platform 3/4 (SE Rlwy)
Henrys Café Bar, Ringers Road (Private)
Nandos, Widmore Road (Nandos)
Partridge, High Street (Fullers)
Richmal Crompton, Westmoreland Place (JDW)
Walkabout, High Street (Private)
Widmore Centre Nightingale Road (Private)
Churchill Theatre, High Street (Private)
Empire Cinema, 2423 High Street (Private)

Chislehurst   ❯   High Street, Car Park

Coney Hall   ❯   Kingsway

Crystal Palace   ❯   Crystal Palace Park
Crystal Palace Caravan Club Site (Caravan Club)

Farnborough   ❯   Church Road

Leaves Green   ❯   Ashmore Lane, car park

Locksbottom   ❯   Pallant Way, off Crofton Road

Orpington   ❯   The Walnuts Precinct, off High Street

Priory Gardens Recreation Ground, Perry Hall Rd
Harvest Moon, High Street (JDW)
Nandos, Nugent Shopping Park (Nandos)
Walnuts Leisure Centre (Private)

Penge, SE20 ❯ High Street, by McDonalds
McDonalds, High Street (McDonalds)
Moon & Stars, High Street (JDW)

Petts Wood ❯ Station Square
Daylight Inn, Station Square (Private)
Sovereign of the Seas, Queensway (JDW)

West Wickham ❯ Glebe Way, by Library
West Wickham Station (SE Rlwy)
Railway Hotel, Red Lodge Road (Private)

CAMDEN (see also Central London)

Camden Town, NW1 ❯ Camden Lock Market (Private)
The Crescent, Camden High Street (Private)
Edward's, Camden High Street (Private)
Ice Wharf, Suffolk Wharf (JDW)
Jongleurs, Camden Lock (Private)

Cricklewood, NW2 ❯ Beaten Docket, Cricklewood Broadway (JDW)

Hampstead, NW3 ❯ Nassington Rd, Athletics Track (City of London)
Vale of Health/East Heath Road (City of London)

Highgate, N6 ❯ Pond Square, South Grove
Millfield Lane, Highgate West Hill (City of London)
Parliament Hill Fields (City of London)

Kentish Town, NW5 ❯ Camden Society, Holmes Road (CP)

Kilburn, NW6 ❯ West End Lane/Mill Lane

Swiss Cottage, NW5 ❯ Queens Crescent/Malden Road

West Hampstead, NW3 ❯ Walkabout, 02 Centre (Private)
Wetherspoons, O2 Centre (JDW)

CROYDON THE CITY OF LONDON (See Central London)

Coulsdon ❯ Farthing Downs (City of London)

Croydon ❯ Croydon Clocktower (Library & Performance hrs)
Wellesley Road, Lunar House
East Croydon Station Platform 3/4 (Southern)
West Croydon Bus Station (TfL)
All Bar One, Park Lane (M&B)
Builders Arms, Leslie Park (Fullers)
Caffe Nero, George Street (Private)
Escapade, High Street (Private)
The George, George Street (JDW)
Goose on the Market, Surrey Street (M&B)
Milan Bar, High Street (JDW)
Nandos, 29 High Street (Nandos)
Nandos, Valley Park Leisure Centre (Nandos)
Porter & Sorter, Station Road East (Marstons)
Ship of Fools, London Road (JDW)
The Skylark, Southend (JDW)
Spread Eagle, Katherine Street (Fullers)
Tiger Tiger, High Street (Private)
Walkabout, Crown Hill (Private)
Yates's Bar, High Street (Yates)

Crystal Palace, SE19 ❯ Postal Order, Westow Street (JDW)
Gala Bingo, Church Road (Gala)

Norbury, SW16 ❯ Moon Under Water, London Road (JDW)

Purley ❯ Foxley Hatch, Russell Hill Road (JDW)
Purley Bowl, Brighton Road (AMF)

**WORKING TOWARDS AN ACCESSIBLE
ENVIRONMENT FOR ALL IN
THE CITY OF LONDON**

The City of London Corporation continues
to promote an accessible and inclusive
environment. The Access Team is working to
improve access to streets, buildings, pedestrian
crossings and parking across the square mile.
To obtain a booklet giving information on access
in the City of London, including wheelchair
accessible public WC facilities, please call the
Access Team on:

Phone: 020 7332 1995
Typetalk: 18001 020 7332 1995
Email: access@cityoflondon.gov.uk

CITY
LONDON

Greater London

Selsdon	❯	Selsdon Library (Library hrs)
		Sir Julian Huxley, Addington Road (JDW)
South Norwood, SE25	❯	William Stanley, High Street (JDW)
Thornton Heath	❯	Flora Sandes, Brigstock Road (JDW)
Upper Norwood	❯	Biggin Woods (Daytime)

EALING

Acton, W3	❯	Acton Green, South Parade
		Goldsmiths Arms, East Acton Lane (Private)
		Red Lion & Pineapple, High Street (JDW)
		Acton & W London College (College) (CP)
Ealing, W5	❯	Walpole Park (April-September)
		Pitshanger Park
		Broadway Shopping Centre (Private)
		Ealing Broadway Station (Gt Western)
		Fox & Goose, Hanger Lane (Fullers)
		The Green, The Green (Private)
		Nandos, Bond Street (Nandos)
		Rose & Crown, St Marys Road (Fullers)
		Sir Michael Balcon, The Mall (JDW)
Greenford	❯	Oldfield Lane South
Hanwell W7	❯	Brent Lodge Park
Park Royal, W3	❯	Nandos, Kendal Avenue (Nandos)
Southall	❯	Southall Park, Southall High St
		The Broadway/Dane Road
		Ealing Hospital, Uxbridge Road (Health Authority)
West Ealing, W13	❯	Deans Gardens, Uxbridge Road
		Drayton Court, The Avenue (Fullers)
		Duke of Kent, Scotch Common (Fullers)

ENFIELD

Edmonton, N9	❯	Craig Park (Park hrs)
		Jubilee Park (Park hrs)
		Edmonton Green Shopping Centre (Private)

Stag & Hounds, Bury Street West (Private)

Enfield ❯
Civic Centre (M&F) (Office hrs)
Enfield Playing Field (Park hrs)
Forty Hall, Forty Hill (Park hrs)
Town Park
Palace Gardens Shopping Centre (2) (Private)
Enfield Town Station (NX East Anglia)
Moon Under Water, Chase Side (JDW)
Robin Hood, The Ridgeway (Private)
Rose & Crown, Clay Hill (Private)

Enfield Highway ❯
Albany Park, Hetford Road
Durants Park, Hertford Road (2)
Turkey Street/Hertford Road

New Southgate, N11 ❯
Arnos Park (Park hrs)

Palmers Green, N13 ❯
Broomfield Park (2) (Park hrs)
Alfred Herring, Green Lanes (JDW)

Ponders End ❯
Recreation Ground, High Street (2)
Picture Palace, Lincoln Road (JDW)

Southgate, N14 ❯
Boundary Playing Fields
Grovelands Park (Park hrs)

Tatem Park (Park hrs)
New Crown, Chase Side (JDW)
White Hart, Chase Road (Private)

Upper Edmonton, N18 ❯
Pymmes Park, Victoria Road (Park hrs)

Gilpins Bell, Fore Street (JDW)

Tatem Park (Park hrs)
New Crown, Chase Side (JDW)
White Hart, Chase Road (Private)

Upper Edmonton, N18 ❯
Pymmes Park, Victoria Road (Park hrs)
Gilpins Bell, Fore Street (JDW)

GREENWICH

Abbey Wood, SE2 ❯
Bostall Gardens (Daylight)

Blackheath, SE3 ❯
Battley Park
Westcombe Park Station (SE Rlwy)

Royal Standard, Vanbrugh Road (Private)

Charlton, SE7   Charlton Station (SE Rlwy)

Eltham, SE9   Avery Hill Park, Bexley Road (Daylight)
Eltham Park South (Daylight)
Eltham Station (SE Rlwy)
New Eltham Station (SE Rlwy)
Bankers Draft, High Street (JDW)

Greenwich, SE10   Cutty Sark Gardens
Rodmere Street (7.00-19.00)
St Alfege Recreation Centre (Centre hrs)
Tourist Information Centre (Centre hrs)
Greenwich Park, Blackheath Gate (Royal Parks)
Greenwich Park, by Play Area (Royal Parks)
Greenwich Station (SE Rlwy)
Maze Hill Station (SE Rlwy)
Gate Clock, Creek Road (JDW)

Mottingham, SE9   Mottingham Station (SE Rlwy)

North Greenwich, SE10 ❯ Ha! Ha! Bar, Entertainment Ave., O2 (Private)
Nandos, UCI, Bugsbys Way (Nandos)
Nandos, O2, Millennium Way (Nandos)

Woolwich, SE18 ❯ Beresford Square (7.00-19.00)
The Ferry (7.00-19.00)
Herbert Road (7.00-19.00)
Vincent Road (7.00-19.00)
Woolwich Arsenal Station (SE Rlwy)
Woolwich Dockyard Station (SE Rlwy)
Great Harry, Wellington Street (JDW)
McDonalds, Powis Street (McDonalds)
Gala Bingo, Powis Street (Gala)

HACKNEY

Dalston, E8 ❯ Birkbeck Road, Ridley Road Market
Kingsland Passage, Dalston Junction
Kingsland Waste
Kingsland Shopping Centre Car Park (Private)
Nandos, Kingsland High Street (Nandos)

Hackney, E8 ❯ Narrow Way, Mare Street
Wilton Way, by Town Hall
St John at Hackney Gardens Inf. Centre (Private)
Baxters Court, Mare Street (JDW)

Hoxton, N1 ❯ Hoxton Market, Stanway Street

Stamford Hill, N16 ❯ Stamford Hill Broadway

Stoke Newington, N16 ❯ Clissold Park (Park hrs)
Newington Green
Nandos, Church Street (Nandos)
Rochester Castle, High Street (JDW)

HAMMERSMITH & FULHAM

Fulham, SW6 ❯ Lillie Road/Fulham Palace Road
Vanston Place, Fulham Broadway
Crabtree, Rainville Road (Private)
Durell, Fulham Road (Private)
Nandos, 20 Fulham Broadway (Nandos)
Oyster Rooms, Fulham Broadway (JDW)
Craven Cottage (Fulham FC)

Hammersmith, W6 ❯ Hammersmith Broadway Centre (2)
Kings Mall Shopping Centre
Ravenscourt Park, Café (9.30-17.30)
Social Services Office, King Street (Office hrs)

Talgarth Road
Hop Poles, King Street (Private)
Old Trout, Broadway (Private)
Plough & Harrow, King Street (JDW)
Rutland, Lower Mall (Private)
William Morris, King Street (JDW)
Hammersmith Apollo (Private)

Shepherds Bush, W12 ❯ Shepherds Bush Green, by Post Office
White City Bus Station (TfL)
Central Bar, West 12 Shopping Centre (JDW)
Nandos, 284 Uxbridge Roiad (Nandos)
Nandos, Westfield Shopping Centre (Nandos)
Walkabout, Shepherds Bush Green (Private)
Cinema, Shepherds Bush Centre (Private)

HARINGEY

Crouch End, N8 ❯ Hatherley Gardens/Haringey Park

Finsbury Park ❯ Finsbury Park Recreation Ground, by Café

Highgate, N6 ❯ Highgate Wood (City of London)
The Gatehouse, North Road (JDW)

Hornsey, N8 ❯ The Tollgate, Turnpike Lane (JDW)

Muswell Hill, N10 ❯ Summerland Gardens Car Park

South Tottenham, N15 ❯ Apex Corner, Seven Sisters Road
St Ann's Road, Chestnut Recreation Ground

Tottenham, N17 ❯ Coombes Croft, nr. Spurs Football Ground (M&F)
Tottenham Hale Station, Platform 2
(NX East Anglia)

Wood Green, N22 ❯ The Mall Shopping City (Private)
The Gate, Buckingham Road (Private)
Wetherspoons, Spouters Corner (JDW)
Yates's Bar, Metroplex Centre (Yates)

HARROW

Edgware ❯ Bob Lawrence Library (Library hrs)
Whitchurch Lane/Buckingham Road
The Mall Broadwalk, Station Road (Private)
Zan Zi Bar, High Street (Private)

Harrow ❯ Greenhill Way, nr. Havelock Place
Harrow Leisure Centre (Centre hrs)
St Anns Shopping Centre (Private)
St George's Shopping (Private)
Harrow Bus Station (TfL)
Castle, West Street (Fullers)
The Junction, Gaydon Way (Private)
Moon on the Hill, Station Road (JDW)
O'Neills, Station Road (M&B)
Rat & Parrot, St Anns Road (Private)
Yates's Bar, Station Road (Yates)

Harrow Weald ❯ High Road
Leefe Robinson VC, Uxbridge Road (Private)

Hatch End ❯ Moon & Sixpence, Uxbridge Road (JDW)

Kenton ❯ Belmont Circle, Kenton Lane
New Moon, Kenton Road (JDW)

North Harrow ❯ Pinner Road

Pinner ❯ Chapel Lane
Caffe Nero, Love Lane (Private)
Village Inn, Rayners Lane (JDW)

Rayners Lane ❯ Rayners Lane, opp. Station

South Harrow ❯ Northolt Road
Nandos, 306 Northolt Road (Nandos)

Stanmore ❯ Stanmore Recreation Ground (Park hrs)
Crazy Horse, Church Road (Private)
Man in the Moon, Buckingham Parade (JDW)

Sudbury Hill ❯ Rising Sun, Greenford Road (Private)

Wealdstone ❯ Gladstone Way MSCP
Harrow & Wealdstone Station (London

Overground)
Goodwill To All, Headstone Drive (Private)

HAVERING

Collier Row ❯ Collier Row Road
Aspen Tree, Gobions Avenue (Greene King)
Bell & Gate, Collier Row Lane (Private)
Colley Rowe Inn, Collier Row (JDW)

Corbetts Tey ❯ Huntsman & Hounds, Ockendon Road (Private)

Cranham ❯ Golden Crane, Avon Road (Private)

Elm Park ❯ Station Parade

Gidea Park ❯ Station Road

Harold Hill ❯ Hilldene Avenue

Havering-atte-Bower ❯ Orange Tree, Orange Tree Inn (Private)

Hornchurch ❯ Appleton Way
Ardleigh & Dragon, Ardleigh Green Rd (Private)
Harrow, Hornchurch Road (Private)
Hogshead, Station Lane (Private)
JJ Moons, High Street (JDW)
Lloyds Bar, High Street (JDW)
Nandos, 111 High Street (Nandos)
Railway, Station Lane (Private)

Rainham ❯ Cherry Tree Lane
Albion, Rainham Road

Romford ❯ South Street
Liberty Shopping Centre (Private)
The Mall Romford (Private)
Debenhams Store, Market Pl (Debenhams)
Romford Station, Platform 4 (NX East Anglia)
Custom House, South Street (Private)
Edwards, South Street (Private)
Moon & Stars, South Street (JDW)
Nandos, The Brewery (Nandos)
Squire, North Street (Private)
Worlds Inn, South Street (JDW)
Yates's Bar, South Street (Yates)

Upminster	❯	Upminster Bridge, Upminster Road Upminster Station, Lower Ticket Office (C2C) Optomist, Hacton Lane (Private)

HILLINGDON

Cowley	❯	Station Road
Devonshire Lodge	❯	Car Park
Eastcote	❯	The Manor, Field End Road (Private)
Harefield	❯	Park Lane, by Library
Hatton Cross	❯	by Underground Station
Hayes	❯	Barra Hall Park Botwell Lane Coldharbour Lane Connaught Recreation Ground St Anselms Road, Town Centre Hayes & Harlington Station (Gt Western) Botwell Inn, Coldharbour Lane (JDW)
Hillingdon	❯	Red Lion, Royal Lane (Fullers)
Ickenham	❯	Community Close Titchenham Inn, Swakeleys Road (JDW)
Northwood	❯	Joel Street [May/June 2010] Oaklands Gate William Jolle, The Broadway (JDW)
Ruislip	❯	High Street Manor Farm JJ Moons, Victoria Road (JDW)
Ruislip Manor	❯	Linden Avenue
Uxbridge	❯	Fairfield Road Pavilions Shopping Centre (Private) Debenhams Store, The Chimes (Debenhams) Good Yarn, High Street (JDW) Nandos, The Chimes (Nandos) White House, Stockley Park (JDW)

HOUNSLOW

Bedfont ❯ Bedfont Library, Staines Road (Library hrs)

Brentford ❯ Half Acre, Brentford High Street
Brentford Station, Waiting Room (SW Trains)
Syon Park, Wyevale Garden Centre (Private)
Kew Bridge Steam Museum (Private)

Chiswick W4 ❯ Hog's Head, Chiswick High Road (Private)
Nandos, 187 Chiswick High Rd (Nandos)
Packhorse & Talbot, Chiswick High Rd (Private)
Paragon Chiswick High Road (Private)
Roebuck, Chiswick High Road (Private)

Cranford ❯ Jolly Waggoner, 618 Bath Road (Private)

Feltham ❯ Feltham Library (Library hrs)
Feltham Station (SW Trains)
Moon on the Square, The Centre (JDW)
Nandos, Longford Shopping Centre (Nandos)
Gala Bingo, Airpark Way (Gala)
Hounslow Urban Farm, Fagg's Road (Private)

Gunnersbury ❯ Gunnersbury Park (Park hrs)

Heston ❯ Rose & Crown, 220 Heston Road (Private)

Heston M4 ❯ Heston Services East, J2/3 M4 (Moto)
Heston Services West, J2/3 M4 (Moto)

Hounslow ❯ Treaty Shopping Centre (2) (Private)
Bullstrode, Lampton Road (Private)
KFC, High Street (KFC)
Moon Under Water, 84 Staines Rd (JDW)
Nandos, High Street (Nandos)
TJB's Café, Treaty Centre (Private)
Yates's Bar, Bath Road (Yates)
Gala Bingo, Staines Road (Gala)
Lampton Sports Centre, Lampton Avenue
(Private)

Isleworth ❯ London Apprentice, Church Street (Private)

Osterley ❯ Hare & Hounds, Windmill Lane (Private)

ISLINGTON (see also Central London)

Archway, N19 〉 Archway Leisure Centre (Centre hrs)

Barnsbury, N1 〉 Albion, Thornhill Road (Private)

Canonbury, N1 〉 The House, Canonbury Road (Private)

Highbury, N5 〉 Highbury Fields, Tennis Courts End
Emirates Stadium (Arsenal FC)

Holloway, N7 〉 Sobell Leisure Centre (Centre hrs)
London Met University, Holloway Rd (University)
Morrison's Store, Holloway Road (Morrison)
The Coronet, Holloway Road (JDW)
James Selby, Holloway Road (Private)

Islington, N1 〉 Council Offices, Upper Street (Office hrs)
Islington Green, Essex Road
White Conduit Street, Chapel Market (8.00-18.00)
N1 Centre, Islington High Street (Private)
The Angel, Islington High Street (JDW)
Glass Works, N1 Centre (JDW)
Steam Passage, Upper Street (Private)
Walkabout, Upper Street (Private)
White Swan, Upper Street (JDW)

Stroud Green, N4 〉 White Lion of Mortimer, Stroud Green Rd (JDW)

**List of Public Conveniences in
Hillingdon with disabled access:**

1. Oaklands Gate, Northwood USL 24/7
2. Park Lane, Harefield USL 24/7
3. Ruislip High Street USL 24/7
4. Community Close, Ickenham USL 24/7
5. Connaught Recreation Ground, Hayes. USL 24/7
6. Coldharbour Lane, Hayes USL 24/7
7. St Anslems Road, Hayes USL 24/7
8. Hatton Cross Tube Station USL 24/7
9. Linden Avenue, Ruislip Manor USL 24/7
10. Botwell Lane, Hayes
    Traditional Style - Monday to Friday 0800 - 1700
11. Manor Farm, Ruislip
    Traditional Style - Monday to Friday 0800 - 1700

USL= Universal Superloo

KENSINGTON & CHELSEA

Kensington, W8 ❯ Holland Park, Ilchester Place (Park hrs)
Kensington High Street, by Odeon
Kensington Town Hall Car Park (Daytime)

North Kensington, W10 ❯ Emslie Hornimans Pleasance, Bosworth Rd (Park hrs)
Portobello Road/Lonsdale Road

Notting Hill, W11 ❯ Kensington Memorial Park, St Marks Rd (Park hrs)
Notting Hill Gate, opp. Cinema
Tavistock Piazza
Westbourne Grove/Colville Road
Duke of Wellington, Portobello Road (Youngs)
The Mitre, Holland Park Avenue (Private)
Nandos, Notting Hill Gate (Nandos)

South Kensington, SW7 ❯ Black Widow, Gloucester Road (Private)
Nandos,117 Gloucester Road (Nandos)

West Brompton, SW10 ❯ Westfield Park

West Kensington, W14 ❯ Kensington, Russell Gardens (Private)

KINGSTON-UPON-THAMES

Chessington ❯ Hook & Chessington Library, Hook Rd (Library hrs)
Chessington Oak, Moore Lane (M&B)
North Star, Hook Road (Private)

For information about Public
Conveniences in the Royal Borough
of Kensington and Chelsea, please
telephone Streetline on **020 7361 3001**
or visit our website at
www.rbkc.gov.uk

THE ROYAL BOROUGH OF
KENSINGTON
AND CHELSEA

Kingston >

Barnfield Youth & Community Centre (Centre hrs)
Bittoms Car Park (Mon-Sat, 7.45-19.00)
Eden Walk Car Park, by Shopmobility
Kingston Crematorium (Opening hrs)
Kingsmeadow Fitness Centre (Centre hrs)
Market Hall, Market Place
The Rose Car Park, Kingston Hall Road
Kingston College, Richmond Road (College)
Cromwell Street Bus Station (TfL)
Kingston Station, Platform 2 (SW Trains)
Bentall Centre (Private)
John Lewis Store, Wood Street (John Lewis)
The Ballroom, Oceana (Private)
British Oak, Richmond Road (Private)
Departure Lounge, Oceana (Private)
Frangos, The Rotunda (Private)
Ha! Ha! Bar, Charter Quay (Private)
King's Tun. Clarence Street (JDW)
Litten Tree, Castle Street (Private)
Old Orleans, The Rotunda, Clarence St (Private)
O'Neill's, Eden Street (M&B)
Gala Bingo, Richmond Road (Gala)
Hawker Leisure Centre (YMCA)

New Malden >

Blagdon Road Car Park
Malden Centre, Cocks Crescent
New Malden Library, Kingston Rd (Library hrs)
Bar Malden, St Georges Square (Marstons)
The Fountain, Malden Road (Private)
Crescent Resource Centre (CP)

Norbiton	❯	Kingston Gate, London Road (Private)
Surbiton	❯	Claremont Road, by Clocktower Victoria Park Surbiton Station, Platforms (SW Trains) Cap in Hand, Hook Rise (JDW) Coronation Hall, St Marks Hill (JDW) Elm Tree, Victoria Street (Private) Hog's Head, Victoria Road (Private) Rat & Parrot, St Marks Hill (Private) Surbiton Flyer, Victoria Road (Fullers)
Tolworth	❯	Tolworth Recreation Centre (Private) Broadway Café Bar, The Broadway (Marstons)

LAMBETH (see also Central London)

Brixton, SW2	❯	Popes Road The Beehive, 407 Brixton Road (JDW)
Clapham, SW4	❯	Revolution, Clapham High Street (Private)
Streatham, SW16	❯	The Rookery, Streatham Common Crown & Sceptre, Streatham Hill Rd (JDW) Holland Tringham, High Road (JDW) Nandos, 6 The High Parade (Nandos)
Vauxhall, SW8	❯	Vauxhall Bus Station (TfL)
West Norwood SE27	❯	Norwood High Street, by Library

LEWISHAM

Blackheath, SE3	❯	Blackheath Grove The Railway, Blackheath Village (Private)
Brockley, SE4	❯	Brockley Barge, Brockley Road (JDW)
Catford, SE6	❯	Catford Broadway/Catford Grove Catford Bridge Station (SE Rlwy) London & Rye, Rushey Green (JDW) Nandos, Rushey Green (Nandos)
Deptford, SE8	❯	Broomhill Park (Park hrs) Giffin Street (7.00-19.00)

Downham ❯ Downham Way/Old Bromley Road

Forest Hill, SE23 ❯ Forest Hill Station Forecourt
The Capitol, London Road (JDW)

Grove Park, SE12 ❯ Chinbrook Road
Grove Park Station (SE Rlwy)

Hither Green, SE13 ❯ Station Hotel, Hither Green (Private)

Kidbrooke SE3 ❯ Kidbrooke Station (SE Rlwy)

Lee, SE12 ❯ Lee Station (SE Rlwy)
The Crown, Burnt Ash Hill (Youngs)
Nando's, Lee High Road (Nandos)
Yates' Bar, Lee High Road (Yates)

Lee Green, SE12 ❯ Sainsbury's Store, Burnt Ash Rd (Sainsbury)
Edmund Halley, Lee Gate Centre (JDW)

Lewisham, SE13 ❯ Lewisham High Street, by Littlewoods
Lewisham Library (Library hrs)
Lewisham Shopping Centre (Private)
Lewisham Station (SE Rlwy)
Marlowes Bar, High Street (Marstons)
Watch House, High Street (JDW)

New Cross, SE14 ❯ New Cross Station (SE Rlwy)
Hobgoblin, New Cross Road (Private)

Sydenham, SE26 ❯
Home Park
Sydenham Station Approach

MERTON

Colliers Wood ❯
Colliers Wood Recreation Ground
Wandle Park, Home Park Road
Nandos, Tandem Centre (Nandos)

Merton Park ❯
John Innes Park, Church Path

Mitcham ❯
Canons Recreation Ground, Madeira Road
Rowan Road Recreation Ground
Tamworth Farm Recreation Ground, London Road
White Lion of Mortimer, London Road (JDW)

Morden ❯
Joseph Hood Recreation Ground, Martin Way

Motspur Park ❯
Sir Joseph Hood Playing Fields (Park hrs)

Raynes Park, SW20 ❯
Cottenham Park Recreation Ground
Edward Rayne, Coombe Lane (JDW)

Roehampton, SW15 ❯
Commons Extension, Robin Hood Lane

West Wimbledon ❯
Holland Gardens

Wimbledon, SW19 ❯
The Broadway/Queens Road (Daytime)
Cannizaro Park, West Side (Park hrs)
Dundonald Recreation Ground
Haydons Road Recreation Ground
South Park Gardens, Dudley Road
Wimbledon Park, Home Park Road (Park hrs)
Centre Court Shopping Centre (Private)
Debenhams Store, Centre Court (Debenhams)
Wimbledon Station, Platforms 1&8 (SW Trains)
Nandos, Russell Road (Nandos)
O'Neill's, The Broadway (M&B)
Walkabout, The Broadway (Private)
Wibbas Down Inn, Gladstone Road (JDW)
Yates's Bar, Hartfield Road (Yates)

NEWHAM

Beckton, E6   ➤   Beckton Park North (Park hrs)
St John's Road Car Park
Asda Superstore (Asda)
Nandos, Gallions Reach Shopping Park (Nandos)

Canning Town, E16   ➤   Rathbone Market, Barking Road
Docklands Campus (University)

East Ham, E6   ➤   Central Park, Cafe (Park hrs)
Clements Road/High Street North
Plashet Park (Park hrs)
Town Hall (Office hrs)
East Ham Leisure Centre, Barking Road (CP)
East Ham Campus, High St South (Newham College)
Millers Well, 419 Barking Road (JDW)
Gala Bingo, Barking Road (Gala)

Forest Gate, E7   ➤   Romford Road/Woodgrange Road
Shaftesbury Road Car Park
Hudson Bay, Upton Lane (JDW)

Manor Park, E12   ➤   Romford Road/Herbert Road
City of London Cemetery (2) (City of London)

Plaistow, E13   ❯
Greengate Street/Barking Road
Hamara Ghar Square
Queens Market
Community Centre, Balaam Street (CP)
Boleyn Ground, Upton Park (West Ham Utd)

Stratford, E15   ❯
Stratford Bus Station (6.00-21.00)
Stratford Campus, Welfare Road (Newham College)
Stratford Shopping Centre (Private)
Stratford Station (TfL)
Golden Grove, The Grove (JDW)
Goose on the Broadway, Broadway (M&B)
Nandos, 1a Romford Road (Nandos)
Swan, The Broadway (Private)
Yates's Bar, The Broadway (Yates)
Gala Bingo, High Street (Gala)

West Ham, E15   ❯
West Ham Lane/Whalebone Lane [Planned]
West Ham Park (City of London)

REDBRIDGE

Barkingside   ❯
Cranbrook Rd, by Park
New Fairlop Oak, Fencepiece Road (JDW)
Gala Bingo, Fairlop Road (Gala)

Chadwell Heath   ❯
Wangey Road (7.30-21.00)
Eva Hart, High Street (JDW)

Clayhall   ❯
Clayhall Park, Longwod Gdns

Gants Hill   ❯
Clarence Avenue (7.30-21.00)

Goodmayes   ❯
High Road/Barley Lane (Mon-Sat, 7.30-18.30)

Hainault   ❯
Hainault Recreation Ground (Park hrs)
Manford Way

Ilford   ❯
Cranbrook Road, nr. The Drive (Mon-Sat, (7.30-18.30) Chapel Road/Roden Street
Horns Road, op.B&Q (Mon-Sat, 7.30-18.30)
Ilford Central Library (Library hrs)
Ilford High Road, Griggs Approach
Ley Street, MSCP

The Mall Ilford (3) (Private)
Clements Road MSCP (Private)
Ilford Station, Overbridge (NX East Anglia)
Great Spoon of Ilford, Cranbrook Rd (JDW)
Nandos, Clements Road (Nandos)

Seven Kings ❯ Aldborough Rd South, opp. Chepstow Cres
(Mon-Sat, Daytime)
High Road, nr Station Car Park (Mon-Sat,
(7.30-18.30)
South Park Road, off Green Lane (7.30-18.30)

South Woodford, E18 ❯ Eastwood Close

Wanstead, E11 ❯ Christchurch Green, off High St (M&F) (7.30-21.00)
Wanstead Park (City of London)
Cuckfield, High Street (Private)
The George, High Street (JDW)

Woodford Green ❯ Hillside Avenue
Johnston Road

RICHMOND-UPON-THAMES

Barnes, SW13 ❯ Red Lion, Castelnau (Private)

Hampton ❯ Bushy Park, by Playground (Royal Parks)
Hampton Court Palace, Tiltyard Restaurant
(Private)

Mortlake, SW14 ❯ Mortlake Station, Platform 2 (SW Trains)

Richmond ❯ Buccleuch Gardens, off Petersham Road
Old Town Hall, Whitaker Avenue
Princes Street, behind Waitrose
Victoria Place
Richmond Station, Lower Level (SW Trains)
Sainsburys Store, Manor Road (Sainsbury)
Edwards, Kew Road (M&B)
The Lot, Duke Street (Private)
New Inn, Petersham Road (Private)
Old Ship, King Street (Youngs)
O'Neills, The Quadrant (M&B)
Orange Tree, Kew Road (Youngs)

Teddington ❯ The Lion, Wick Road (Private)

Twickenham	❯	Twickenham Station, Platform 3 (SW Trains) George, King Street (Private) Hook Line & Sinker, York Street (Fullers) William Webb Ellis, London Road (JDW) St Margaret, St Margarets Road (Private)
Whitton	❯	Whitton Library Car Park Whitton Sports & Fitness Centre (Centre hrs)

SOUTHWARK (see also Central London)

Bermondsey, SE1	❯	All Bar One, Butlers Wharf (M&B) Pommelers Rest, Tower Bridge Rd (JDW)
Camberwell, SE5	❯	Fox on the Hill, Denmark Hill (JDW) Gala Bingo, Camberwell Road (Gala)
Dulwich, SE21	❯	Dulwich Park, Pavilion Café (Park hrs)
East Dulwich, SE22	❯	East Dulwich Grove, nr. Rye Lane Sainsbury's Store, Dog Kennel Hill (Sainsbury)
Elephant & Castle, SE1	❯	Rockingham Arms, Metro Central Heights (JDW)
Peckham, SE15	❯	Kentish Drovers, Peckham High St (JDW)
Rotherhithe, SE16	❯	Southwark Park Café (Park hrs) Canada Water Bus Station (TfL) Surrey Quays Retail Park (2) (Private) Quebec Curve, Redriff Road (Marstons) Surrey Docks, Lower Road (JDW) Gala Bingo, Surrey Quays (Gala)

SUTTON

Carshalton	❯	Grove Park, by Café (Daytime) Oaks Park (Daytime)
Cheam	❯	Cheam Park, Cheam Park Way (Daytime) Nonsuch Park, by Mansion Café (Epsom & Ewell)
North Cheam	❯	Nonsuch Inn, 552 London Road (JDW) Woodstock, Stonecot Hill (Private)
Rosehill	❯	Mecca Bingo, Bishopsford Road (Mecca)

Sutton ⊗ St Nicholas Centre (2) (Private)
Morrisons Store, High Street (Morrisons)
Caffe Nero, Carshalton Road (Private)
Cock & Bull, High Street (Fullers)
The Grapes, High Street (JDW)
Moon on the Hill, Hill Road (JDW)

Wallington ⊗ Beddington Park, Church Road (Daytime)
Mellows Park (Daytime)
Whispering Moon, Woodcote Road (JDW)

TOWER HAMLETS

Bethnal Green, E2 ⊗ Nandos, 366 Bethnal Green Road (Nandos)

Bow, E3 ⊗ Armagh Road Local Housing Office (Office hrs)
Heylyn Square Local Housing Office (Office hrs)
Thames Magistrates Court (Courts Service)
Jongleurs, Bow Wharf (Private)
Match Maker, 580 Roman Road (JDW)
Morgan Arms, Morgan Street (Private)

Canary Wharf E14 ⊗ Jubilee Place Mall (Private)
All Bar One, South Colonade (M&B)
Café Rouge, Mackenzie Walk (Private)
Cat & Canary, Fishermans Walk (Fullers)
Fine Line, Fishermans Walk (Fullers)
Nandos, Jubilee Place   (Nandos)
Pizza Express, Cabot Place East (Private)
Slug & Lettuce, South Colonnade (Private)
Wagamamas, Jubilee Place (Private)

Limehouse E14 ⊗ Oporto, West India Dock Rd (Private)

Mile End, E1 ⊗ Half Moon, Mile End Road (JDW)
Hayfield, Mile End Road (Private)
Nandos, 9-25 Mile End Road (Nandos)

Poplar, E14 ⊗ East India Dock Road/Burdett Road
Local Housing Office, Market Square
Gun, Coldharbour (Private)

Wapping, E1 ⊗ Prospect of Whitby", Wapping Wall (Private)

West India Quay, E14 ⊗ Bar 38, Hertsmere Road (Private)
The Ledger Building, Hertsmere Road (JDW)

Whitechapel, E1 ⊗ Whitechapel Market
Goodmans Fields, Mansell Street (JDW)

WALTHAM FOREST

Chingford, E4   ❯
Albert Crescent
Royal Hunting Lodge (City of London)
Sainsbury's Store, Walthamstow Ave (Sainsbury)
Chingford Station, off Platform 2 (NX East Anglia)
Green Man, The Ridgway (Private)
King's Ford, Chingford Mount Road (JDW)
Queen Elizabeth, Forest Side (Private)
Station House, Station Road (Marstons)

Leyton, E10   ❯
Tesco Store, 825 High Road (Tesco)
The Drum, 557 Lea Bridge Road (JDW)
Gala Bingo, Lea Bridge Road (Gala)

Leytonstone, E11T   ❯
esco Store, Leytonstone High Rd (Tesco)
Leytonstone Bus Station, Church Road (TfL)
Walnut Tree, 857 High Road (JDW)

Walthamstow, E17
The Mall Walthamstow (Private)
Walthamstow Bus Station, Selborne Rd (TfL)

WANDSWORTH

Balham, SW12   ❯
Jackdaw & Rook, Balham High Rd (Fullers)
Moon Under Water, Balham High Rd (JDW)

Battersea, SW11   ❯
Station Approach, Clapham Junction
Clapham Junction Station, Subway (SW Trains)
The Asparagus, Falcon Road (JDW)
Bank, Northcote Road (Fullers)
Duck, Battersea Rise (Private)
Falcon, St John's Hill (Private)
Jongleurs, Lavender Gardens (Private)
Nandos, Northcote Road (Nandos)
Northcote, Northcote Road (Private)
Prince Albert, Albert Bridge Road (Private)
Revolution, Lavender Hill (Private)

Putney, SW15   ❯
Putney Bridge Road/Putney High Street
Putney Vale Cemetery (Cemetery hrs)
Exchange Shopping Centre (Private)
Cedar Tree, Putney Bridge Road (Private)
Old Spotted Horse, Putney High Street (Youngs)
The Railway, Upper Richmond Rd (JDW)
Real Greek Souvlaki, Putney High St (Private)
Walkabout, Putney High Street (Private)

Southfields, SW18 ❯ Magdalen Road/Garratt Lane
Grid Inn, Replingham Road (JDW)

Tooting, SW17 ❯ Tooting Bec Common, Dr Johnson Avenue
Tooting Broadway/Garratt Lane
A Bar 2 Far, Mitcham Road (Private)
J J Moons, Tooting High Street (JDW)
Kings Head, Upper Tooting Road (Private)
McDonalds, Mitcham Road (McDonalds)
Mitre Hotel, Mitcham Road (Private)
Nandos, 224 Upper Tooting Rd (Nandos)
Tramshed, Mitcham Road (Private)

Wandsworth, SW18 ❯ Garratt Lane/Magdalen Road
Wandsworth High St, by Southside Centre
Nandos, Southside Shopping Centre (Nandos)
Queen Adelaide, Putney Bridge Road (Private)
Rose & Crown, Wandsworth High Street (Private

WESTMINSTER (See also Central London)

Bayswater, W2 ❯ Nandos, 63 Westbourne Grove (Nandos)

Maida Vale, W9 ❯ Elgin Bar & Grill, Elgin Avenue (Private)

St Johns Wood, NW8 ❯ Salisbury Street/Church Street (7.30-18.00)
Wellington Place, by Lords (10.00-18.00)
Lords Cricket Ground (Matchdays) (MCC)

SOUTH EAST ENGLAND

ADUR

Lancing ❯
Beach Green
Yew Tree Close, South Street

Lancing Beach ❯
Shopsdam Road
Widewater, West Beach Road

Shoreham Beach ❯
Fort Haven

Shoreham-by-Sea ❯
Adur Recreation Ground, Brighton Road
Beach Green, Beach Road
Buckingham Park
Civic Centre, Ham Road
Middle Street

Southwick ❯
Southwick Beach, Basin Road (F only)
Southwick Square (Mon-Sat)

ARUN

Aldwick ❯
Marine Park Gardens
West Park

Angmering ❯
Haskins Roundstone Garden Centre (Private)

Arundel ❯
Crown Yard
Mill Road

Bognor Regis ❯
Bedford Street
East Promenade Foreshore Office
Hotham Park, High Street
London Road Car Park
Regis Centre
Waterloo Square
Bognor Regis Station (Southern)
Hatters Inn, Queensway (JDW)
Rowan Park Caravan Site (Caravan Club)

Felpham ❯
Blakes Road
Southdowns, Felpham Way (Private)

Littlehampton ❯
Arun Civic Centre (Office hrs)

Coastguard Toilets
Mewsbrook Park
Norfolk Road
St Martins Car Park
Littlehampton Station, Ticket Office (Southern)
George Inn, Surrey Street (JDW)

Middleton-on-Sea Shrubbs Field

Pagham Sandy Road

Rustington Broadmark Avenue (Parish Council)
Churchill Car Park (Parish Council)
The Street, by Church (Parish Council)
Woodlands Centre, Recreation Ground
(Parish Council)

ASHFORD

Ashford Bank Street
Church Road
Forge Lane, New Rents
Park Street/North Street
St Johns Lane
County Mall Shopping Centre (Private)
Sainsburys Store, Bybrook (Sainsbury)
Ashford International Station (SE Rlwy)
County Hotel, High Street (JDW)
Ashford Bowl, Station Road (AMF)

Chilham Taylors Hill Car Park

Tenterden Recreation Ground Road
St Michaels Recreation Ground
Station Road

Woodchurch Front Road Car Park

BRIGHTON & HOVE

Aldrington Recreation Ground, Saxon Rd (8.00-16.00,
later in summer)

Brighton & Hove Black Rock (Summer only, 9.30-18.00)

Seafront ❯

King Alfred, Kings Esplanade (8.00-20.00, later in summer)
Kings Esplanade, op. First Avenue (8.00-20.00, later in summer)
Lagoon, Kingsway (8.00-17.00, later in summer)
Lower Prom, E of Brighton Pier (Summer, 8.00-20.00)
Lower Prom, West Pier Play Area (Summer, 8.00-17.00)
Lower Prom, West Street (8.00-18.00, later in summer)
Madeira Drive, Colonnade (8.00-18.00, later in summer)
Madeira Drive, Peter Pan Play Area (10-17, later in summer)
Western Esplanade, Kingsway (8.00-17.00, later in summer)
Brighton Pier, by café (Private)
Concord 2, Madeira Hall (Private)
Terraces Bar, Madeira Drive (Private)

Brighton Town Centre ❯

Booth Museum, Dyke Road (Museum hrs)
Brighton History Centre, Church Street (Centre hrs)
Brighton Museum & Art Gallery (Museum hrs)
Dyke Road Park (10.00-16.00, later in Summer)
Jubilee Library, Church Street (Library hrs)
King Place (7.00-20.00, later in summer)
The Lanes, Black Lion Street (8.00-20.00, later in summer)
Old Steine (8.00-20.00, later in summer)
Prince Regent Swimming Complex (Centre hrs)
Providence Place, Car Park (8.00-20.00, later in summer)
Queens Park, West Drive (10.00-20.00, longer in summer)
Royal Pavilion (Opening hrs)
Royal Pavilion Gardens (M&F) (8.00-20.00, later in summer)
Brighton Law Courts (Courts Service)
Bright Helm, West Street (JDW)
Browns, Ship Street (Private)
Browns Restaurant, Duke Street (Private)
Caffe Nero, Prince Albert Street (Private)
Curve Bar, Gardner Street (Private)
Ha! Ha! Bar, Pavilion Buildings (Private)
Nandos, 34 Duke Street (Nandos)

Standard, West Street (Private)
Walkabout, West Street (Private)
Yates's Bar, West Street (Yates)
Duke of Yorks Cinema, Preston Circus (Private)

Brighton Marina

Mermaid Walk (Private)
Karmer, Waterfront (Private)
West Quay, Brighton Marina Village (JDW)
BowlPlex (Private)

East Brighton

Blakers Park, Cleveland Road (10-18.00)
Moulscombe Community Centre (Centre hrs)
Patcham Library (Library hrs)
Stanley Deeson Leisure Centre (Centre hrs)
Stanmer Village (8.00-18.00, later in summer)
Whitehawk Library (Library hrs)
Wild Park (Summer and Weekends, 10.00-18.00)
Withdean Sports Centre (Centre hrs)
Sheepcote Valley Caravan Park (Caravan Club)

Hangleton

Grenadier, Hangleton Road (8.00-20.00,
later in summer)
Hangleton Library, West Way (Library hrs)

Hove

Goldstone Villas/Eaton Villas (8.00-20.00,
later in summer)
Hove Library (Library hrs)
Hove Museum & Art Gallery (Museum hrs)
Hove Park (8.00-16.00, later in summer)
Hove Recreation Ground (8.00-16.00,
later in summer)
Norton Road (8.00-20.00, later in summer)
St Ann's Well Gardens (8.00-16.00, later in summer)
West Blatchington Windmill (Business hrs)
Hove Station, Platform (Southern)
Station, Goldstone Villas (Private)

Kemptown

Upper Rock Gardens (7.00-20.00, later in summer)
Gala Bingo, Freshfield Business Pk. (Gala)

Ovingdean

Undercliff (10.00-16.00, later in summer)

Portslade

Easthill Park (10.00-16.0, longer in summer)
Foredown Tower (Business hrs)
Mile Oak Library (Library hrs)
Portslade Library (Library hrs)

Station Road (8.00-20.00, later in summer)
Victoria Recreation Ground (8.00-16.00, later in summer)
Victoria Road (8.00-17.00)

Preston Park ❯ Chalet (8.00-16.00, later in summer)
Preston Manor (Business hrs)
Rotunda (8.00-16.00, later in summer)

Rottingdean ❯ Rottingdean Recreation Ground (8.00-20.00, later in summer)
Undercliff (7.00-20.00, later in summer)

Saltdean ❯ Undercliff Walk (8.00-17.00, later in summer)

CANTERBURY

Canterbury ❯ Best Lane
Canterbury Lane
City Council Offices, Military Road (Office hrs)
Longport
Pound Lane
St Peter's Place
Toddlers Cove (April-early October)
Wincheap Park
Worthgate
BHS, Marlowe Arcade (BHS)
Debenhams Store, Guildhall Sq (Debenhams)
Sainsbury's Store, Kingsmead Rd (Sainsbury)
Sidney Cooper Gallery, St Peters St (Gallery hrs)
Canterbury East Station, Platform 2 (SE Rlwy)
Canterbury West Station, Platform 1 (SE Rlwy)
Ha! Ha! Bar, St Margarets Street (Private)
Nandos, 46 St Peters Street (Nandos)

Fordwich ❯ George & Dragon, King Street (Private)

Herne Bay ❯ Bandstand
Beltinge
Council Offices, William Street (Office hrs)
Hampton Pier
Hampton Pleasure Gardens (Easter-early Oct)
Herne Bay Cemetery
Herne Village, Cherry Orchard
Kings Hall
Market Street

Pier Entrance
Reculver Country Park
St George's
William Street
The Saxon Shore, Central Parade (JDW)

Upstreet ❯ Grove Ferry Picnic Site (Kent CC)

Whitstable ❯ Blue Anchor
Faversham Road (Easter-early Oct)
Harbour Street
Horse Bridge
Priest & Sow
St Anne's
St John's
Skinners Alley
Tankerton Beach
Whitstable Station, Platform 1 (SE Rlwy)
Whitstable Bowl, Tower Parade (AMF)

CHICHESTER

Bosham ❯ Bosham Lane Car Park (Daytime)

Bracklesham Bay ❯ Bracklesham Beach Car Park
Lively Lady, Stocks Lane (Private)

Chichester ❯ Avenue de Chartres MSCP (Daytime)
Cathedral Way (Daytime)
East Pallant Car Park (Daytime)
Market Road Car Park (Daytime)
Northgate Car Park (Daytime)
Portfield Cemetery (F only) (Cemetery hrs)
Priory Park (7.30-dusk)
Tower Street (Daytime)
St Martins Car Park (City Council)
Chichester Cathedral (Cathedral)
Chichester Station, Platform 1 (Southern)
Chicago Rock Café, Chichester Gate (Private)
Dolphin & Anchor, West Street (JDW)
Gatehouse, Chichester Gate (JDW)
Globe Inn, Southgate (Private)
Nandos, Chichester Gate (Nandos)
Slug & Lettuce, Southgate (Private)
The Vestry, Southgate (Private)

Cobnor ❯ Footpath Car Park (Harbour Conservancy)

East Wittering ❯ Bracklesham Lane Car Park (Daytime)
Kingfisher Parade (Daytime)

Fishbourne ❯ Roman Palace, Car Park (Private)
Bulls Head (Private)

Goodwood ❯ Goodwood Racecourse (4) (Private)

Midhurst ❯ Grange Road Car Park (Daytime)
North Street Car Park (Daytime)
The Wheatsheaf, Wool Lane (Private)

Petworth ❯ Town Centre Car Park (Daytime)

Selsey ❯ East Beach Amenity Area (Daytime)
East Street (Daytime
Hillfield Road (Daytime)
Lifeboat Station, Kingsway (Daytime)

Sidlesham ❯ Pagham Nature Reserve (W Sussex CC)

West Itchenor ❯ The Street (F only)

West Wittering ❯ Marine Drive Car Park (Daytime)
Pound Road (Daytime)
Pavillion Restaurant (Private)

CRAWLEY

Bewbush ❯ Dorsten Square

Broadfield ❯ Broadfield Barton Car Park
Buchan Country Park (W Sussex CC)

Crawley Town Centre ❯ The Boulevard Car Park
Bus Station, Friary Way
Ifield Road
County Mall Shopping Centre (Private)
Crawley Station, Platform 1 (Southern)
Bar Med, High Street (Private)
Coffee Republic, Queensway (Private
Jubilee Oak, High Street (JDW)
Liquid Envy, Station Way (Private)

Nandos, Crawley Leisure Park (Nandos)
Rat & Parrot, High Street (Private)
Longley Building (Cent Sussex College)
Don Munro Block (Cent Sussex College)
Dartford Station (SE Rlwy)
Crush, Spital Street (Private)
Flying Boat, Spital Street (JDW)
Litten Tree, Spital Street (Private)
Paper Moon, High Street (JDW)
Royal Victoria & Bull, High Street (Private)
Tollgate, High Street (Private)
Gala Bingo, Spital Street (Gala)

Greenhithe   Greenhithe Station (SE Rlwy)

Longfield   Waitrose car park (Private)

DOVER

Ash   Village Car Park, The Street

Deal   Deal Pier
King Street
Kingsdown Road/Granville Road
Town Hall

Dover   Buckland Bridge
The Clock Tower
East Cliff
Kearsney Abbey

Best wishes from

CRAWLEY
BOROUGH COUNCIL

Maison Dieu Gardens Stembrook Car Park
White Cliffs Visitor Centre (Nat. Trust)
Charlton Shopping Centre (Private)
Dover Priory Station, Platform 1 (SE Rlwy)
Eight Bells, Cannon Street (JDW)
Millers, Marine Parade (Private)
Gala Bingo, Biggin Street (Gala)

Sandwich ❍ The Quay

St Margarets at Cliffe ❍ St Margarets Bay

Wingham ❍ Village Car Park

EASTBOURNE

Beachy Head ❍ Beachy Head Car Park

Eastbourne ❍ The Archery, Chanel View Road
Bandstand, Upper Promenade (2)
Bandstand, Lower Promenade
Coach Station, Junction Road
Devonshire Park, Congress Car Park (2)
Fishermen's Green
Helen Gardens, rear of Pavilion
Holywell, Lower Promenade
Hyde Gardens, by Tourist Information Centre
Pier, Lower Promenade
Princes Park, by Café
Redoubt, by Bowls Pavilion
Arndale Shopping Centre (3) (Private)
Enterprise Shopping Centre, car park (Private)
Eastbourne Station, Concourse (Southern)
Wagamama, The Heart (Private)

West Molesey ❍ Recreation Ground, Walton Road

Weybridge ❍ Churchfield Road (Daytime)
High Street, behind shops
Brooklands Museum (Private)

ELMBRIDGE

Claygate ❍ Recreation Ground, Church Road (Daytime)

Cobham ▶ Hollyhedge Road
Chez Gerard, Oakdene Parade (Private)

East Molesey ▶ Molesey Lock, Hurst Road
Walton Road Car Park
Hampton Court Station (SW Trains)
Prince of Wales, Bridge Road (Greene King)

Esher ▶ High Street
Marquis of Granby, Portsmouth Rd (Private)
Sandown Park Racecourse (Racedays) (Private)

Hersham
▶ Hersham Green Shopping Centre (Private)

Walton-on-Thames ▶ Cowey Sale, Walton Bridge
Walton Library, The Heart (Library hrs) (Surrey CC)
Ashley Park, Ashley Park Road (Ember Inns)
Nandos, 7 The Heart (Nandos)
The Regent, Church Street (JDW)
Wagamama, The Heart (Private)

West Molesey ▶ Recreation Ground, Walton Road

Weybridge	❯	Churchfield Road (Daytime) High Street, behind shops Brooklands Museum (Private)

EPSOM & EWELL

Epsom	❯	Alexandra Recreation Ground (Daytime) Epsom Town Hall (Office hrs) Horton Country Park, Horton Lane (Daytime) The Mall Ashley (Private) Assembly Rooms, High Street (JDW) Nandos, The Oaks Square (Nandos) Yates's Bar, Derby Square (Yates)
Epsom Downs	❯	Tattenham Corner (Daytime)
West Ewell	❯	Poole Road Recreation Ground (Daytime)

GRAVESHAM

Gravesend	❯	Anglesea Shopping Centre, Clive Road Borough Market, Queen Street Gordon Promenade St George's Centre (Shopping hrs) Visitor Centre, St Georges Square (Centre hrs) Woodlands Park, Dashwood Road [Temp closed] Debenhams Store, New Road (Debenhams) Pembroke, King Street (Barracuda) Robert Pocock, Windmill Street (JDW)
Higham	❯	School Lane
Meopham	❯	Camer Park, Camer Park Road Wrotham Road/Pitfield Drive

GUILDFORD

Ash Common	❯	Recreation Ground (Parish Council)
Burpham	❯	Sutherland Memorial Park (Park hrs)
Guildford	❯	Allen House, by York Road MSCP (7.00-19.00) Bedford Road Car Park

Farnham Road MSCP (7.00-19.00)
Shalford Park, Shalford Road (7.00-19.00)
Stoke Park, by Nurseries (7.00-19.00)
Stoke Park, by Challenger Centre (7.00-17.00)
Stoke Park, Tennis Courts (7.00-17.00)
Tunsgate, Guildford High Street (7.30-19.00)
Ward Street (7.30-19.00)
Woodbridge Road (7.00-19.00)
Debenhams Store, Millbrook (Debenhams)
Guildford Station, Platform 2 (SW Trains)
George Abbot, High Street/Riverside (Private)
Ha! Ha! Bar, North Street (Private)
Nandos, Friary Street (Nandos)
Old Orleans, Wayside Square (Private)
Rodboro Buildings, Bridge Street (JDW)
Stoke, Stoke Road (Private)

Ripley ◉ High Street

Shere ◉ Middle Street (Parish Council)

HASTINGS

Hastings ◉ Alexandra Park, Tennis Pavilion
Falaise Road
Hastings Country Park, Coastguard Lane
Hastings Country Park, Helipad
Lifeboat House, The Stade
Rock a Nore Road
Hastings Station, Ticket Hall (SE Rlwy)

John Logie Baird, Havelock Road (JDW)
Yates's Bar, Robertson Street (Yates)

Ore ⊙ Ore Village, Fairlight Road

St Leonards ⊙ Warrior Square
Royal Hotel (Private)

HORSHAM

Amberley ⊙ Chalk Pits (Daytime)
Houghton Bridge Tea Garden (Daytime)

Billingshurst ⊙ Mill Lane Car Park

Bramber ⊙ The Street Car Park

Dial Post ⊙ Honeybridge Caravan Park (Private)

Henfield ⊙ High Street Car Park

Horsham ⊙ The Forum, Lower Tanbridge Way (Daytime)
North Parade Boxing Club (Club hrs)
Piries Place Car Park (Daytime)
Swan Walk Shopping Centre (Private)
Green Dragon, Bishopric (Private)
Lynd Cross, Springfield Road (JDW)

Southwater ⊙ Southwater Country Park (Park hrs)

Steyning ⊙ High Street Car Park
Steyning Centre

Washington ⊙ Village Hall

LEWES

Ditchling ⊙ Village Hall Car Park

Glynde ⊙ Recreation Ground

Lewes ⊙ Greyfriars
Market Lane
Southover Grange Gardens (8.00-dusk)
Western Road

The Dorset, Malling Street (Harveys)

Newhaven ❯ Fort Road
Lower Place
Newhaven Fort

Peacehaven ❯ Meridian Centre (9.00-17.00)
Peacehaven Leisure Centre
Roderick Avenue

Ringmer ❯ Village Hall

Seaford ❯ The Buckle
Martello Tower
Place Lane
Salts Recreation Ground

MAIDSTONE

Allington ❯ Mid Kent Shopping Centre (8.30-18.00)

Aylesford ❯ Cobtree Park, Ranger Centre (7.00-16.30)

Maidstone ❯ Brenchley Gardens (M&F) (Daytime)
Church Street (M&F)
Clare Park, Tonbridge Road (Park hrs)
Corn Exchange, Market Buildings (7.00-21.00)
Fairmeadow (7.00-20.00)
Lockmeadow Market Centre (7.00-16.00)
Mote Park (2)
Palace Avenue
Parkwood Shopping Centre, Wallis Avenue
Penenden Heath Road
South Park (7.00-18.00)
Fremlin Walk, Earl Street (Private)
Fremlin Walk, off Week Street (Private)
The Mall Chequers, by Bus Station (Private)
Royal Star Arcade (Private)
Caffe Nero, King Street (Private)
Chicago Rock Café, High Street (Private)
Liquid, Lockmeadow Enterta\inment Centre (Private)
Muggleton Inn, High Street (JDW)
Nandos, 29 Earl Street (Nandos)
Old Orleans, Lockmeadow (Private)
Society Rooms, Week Street (JDW)

Zebra Bar, King Street (Private)
Gala Bingo, Lower Stone Street (Gala)
Maidstone Bowl, King Street (AMF)

Headcorn > Kings Road, Days Green (7.00-21.00)
Headcorn Station (SE Rlwy)

Lenham > Maidstone Road (7.00-18.00)

Marden > High Street, Library Car Park (7.00-21.00)

Staplehurst > Bell Lane (7.00-18.00)
Staplehurst Shopping Parade (7.00-17.00)

Sutton Valence > North Street, by Village Hall (6.00-118.00)

Yalding > The Lees

MEDWAY

Chatham > Capstone Farm Country Park
Luton Recreation Ground, Capstone Road
(Matchdays)
Pentagon, Ground Level (Private)
Chatham Station (SE Rlwy)
Nandos, Dickens World (Nandos)
Old Ash Tree, Rainham Road (Private)
Gala Bingo, High Street (Gala)

Cliffe > The Buttway (8.00-18.00)

Gillingham > Canterbury Street (M&F) (8.00-18.00)
Sappers Walk, High Street
Riverside Country Park
Strand, Pier Road (8.00-18.00, later in Summer)
Gillingham Station (SE Rlwy)
Priestfield Stadium (7) (Matchdays) (Private)

Hempstead > Hempstead Valley Centre (2) (Private)

Hoo > Stoke Road

Lower Upnor > The Waterfront

Parkwood > Parkwood Green (8.00-18.00)

Rainham	◗	Shopping Precinct, Longley Rd (8.00-18.00) Rainham Station (SE Rlwy)
Rainham M2	◗	Medway Services, Juncts 4/5 (Moto)
Rochester	◗	Acorn Wharf Coach Park (8.00-18.00, later in Summer) Castle Gardens (8.00-18.00, later in Summer) Northgate (8.00-18.00, later in Summer) Golden Lion, High Street (JDW)
Strood	◗	Newark Yard McDonalds, Commercial Road (McDonalds) Gala Bingo, Chariot Way (Gala)
Twydall Green	◗	Shopping Centre (M&F) (8.00-18.00)
Walderslade	◗	Sherwood Oak, Robin Hood Lane (Private)

MID SUSSEX

Ardingly	◗	High Street (Parish Council)
Burgess Hill	◗	Janes Lane Recreation Ground Pavilion The Martlets Shopping Centre, by Library St Johns Park
Cuckfield	◗	Cuckfield Recreation Ground (April-Sept) Broad Street Car Park (Parish Council)
Devils Dyke	◗	by Devils Dyke Hotel (Private)
East Grinstead	◗	King Street Car Park Mount Noddy Recreation Ground Caffe Nero, High Street (Private) Old Mill, Dunnings Road (Harveys) Ounce & Ivy Bush, The Atrium (JDW)
Handcross	◗	Red Lion, High Street (Private)
Hassocks	◗	Adastra Park, Keymer Road
Haywards Heath	◗	The Orchards Shopping Centre Car Park Victoria Park, South Road The Heath, Sussex Road (Harveys)

Lindfield	⮞	Denmans Lane Car Park (Parish Council)

MOLE VALLEY

Ashtead	⮞	Memorial Car Park, off High Street
Bookham	⮞	Lower Shott Car Park off A246
Box Hill	⮞	A24, Car Park opp. Burford Bridge Hotel (Surrey CC)
Dorking	⮞	St Martins Walk, Church Square (Private)
Leatherhead	⮞	Swan Shopping Centre Leatherhead Station (Southern) Edmund Tylney, High Street (JDW) Penny Black, North Street (Youngs)

REIGATE & BANSTEAD

Banstead	⮞	High Street Car Park (8.00-19.00) Lady Neville Recreation Park (8.00-19.00) The Woolpack (Private)
Earlswood	⮞	Earlswood Lakes, Woodhatch Road (7.30-17.00)
Horley	⮞	Consort Way Jack Fairman, Victoria Road (JDW)
Merstham		Aldersted Heath Caravan Club Site (Caravan Club)
Redhill	⮞	Station Road, by McDonalds The Sun, London Road (JDW)
Reigate	⮞	Bell Street, by supermarket (8.00-19.00)
Walton-on-the Hill	⮞	The Chequers, Chequers Road (Youngs)

ROTHER

Battle	⮞	Market Square, by Supermarket Mount Street Car Park Normanhurst Court Caravan Site (Caravan Club)

Bexhill ⊙ Devonshire Square
East Parade
Egerton Park
Little Common Roundabout
Manor Barn, by Car Park
Marina, Channel View East
Normans Bay (Easter to October)
Polegrove Grandstand
Sidley
West Parade

Burwash ⊙ Car Park

Camber ⊙ Central Car Park (Easter-October)
West Car Park (Easter-October)

For more information telephone
our Council Helpline on
01737 276000

Banstead
High Street Car Park (0800-1800)
Lady Neville Recreation Ground (0800-1500)
'The Woolpack' PH (Private)
Earlswood Earlswood Lakes, Woodhatch Road.
Horley Consort Way (0800-1800)
Redhill
Station Road, by McDonalds
opp Bus Station (Private)
Reigate
Bell Street, by Supermarket (0800-1800)
Reigate Hill, Car Park (0800-1800)

For more information
on public facilities,
why not telephone for
more details before
you travel?

**Please telephone
for all enquiries:**

Rother
District Council

01424 787 000

Iden	❯	Village Hall (Hall Committee)
Pett	❯	Pett Level Car Park Fairlight Wood Caravan Park (Caravan Club)
Robertsbridge	❯	Car Park
Rye	❯	Station Approach, Crownfield Gun Gardens Lucknow Place The Strand
Sedlescombe	❯	Car Park
Winchelsea	❯	Winchelsea Town Winchelsea Beach (Summer)

RUNNYMEDE

| Chertsey | ❯ | off Guildford Street |

SEVENOAKS

Edenbridge	❯	Market Yard Car Park (Town Council)
Farningham	❯	Pied Bull, High Street (Private)
Ide Hill	❯	Wheatsheaf Hill Woodman, Whitley Row (Private)
Kemsing	❯	St Edith's Hall, High Street
Leigh	❯	Crandells
New Ash Green	❯	Upper Street
North Kirby	❯	Westminster Field, The Street (Parish Council)
Otford	❯	High Street (Parish Council)
Penshurst	❯	High Street
Sevenoaks	❯	Bus Station, High Street Lower St Johns Car Park

Upper St Johns Hill
The Vine House (Town Council)
Sevenoaks Station, Ticket Hall (SE Rlwy)
Oak Tree, High Street (Barracuda)
The Sennockian, High Street (JDW)
Slug & Lettuce, High Street (Private)

Shoreham ❯ Rangers Lodge, St Andrews Wood
High Street (Parish Council)

Sundridge ❯ White Horse, Main Street (Private)

Swanley ❯ Station Road
Swanley Park, New Barn Rd (Town Council)

Westerham ❯ Fullers Hill (Parish Council)

SHEPWAY

Cheriton ❯ Somerset Road

Densole ❯ Blackhorse Farm Caravan Club Site (Caravan Club)

Dymchurch ❯ High Street

Folkestone ❯ Leas Cliff Hall, The Leas
Pleydell Gardens
Radnor Park, Cheriton Road
Roman Remains, East Cliff (Summer)
The Stade, Folkestone Harbour
Sunny Sands, Coronation Parade (Summer)
Toll Gate, Lower Sandgate Road
Folkestone Central Station (SE Rlwy)
Samuel Peto, Rendezvous St (JDW)

Greatstone ❯ Jolly Fisherman, Coast Drive

Hythe ❯ Chapel Street
Cinque Ports, Stade Street
Marine Parade, Saltwood Gardens (Summer)
Prospect Road

Lydd ❯ Coronation Square
Lade Car Park

New Romney		Car Park, Church Road
St Marys Bay		High Knocke Car Park
West Hythe		Daleacres Caravan Club Site (Caravan Club)

SPELTHORNE

Ashford		Church Road, by MSCP Royal Hart", Church Road (Private)
Laleham		Laleham Park, Pavilion Kiosk
Shepperton		Shepperton Lock, Towpath
Staines		Memorial Gardens, opp Debenhams Elmsleigh Shopping Centre (2) (Private) Blue Anchor, High Street (Private) The George, High Street (JDW) Litten Tree (Private) Nandos, Two Rives (Nandos) Que Pasa, Tillys Lane (Marstons)
Sunbury		Walled Garden Sunbury Cross Shopping Centre (Private)

SURREY HEATH

Bagshot		Park Street
Camberley		Knoll Road by MSCP, behind Theatre Martindale Avenue, Heatherside Watchetts Park (Daytime) The Mall Main Square (Private) Claude Du Vall, High Street (JDW) Que Pasa, High Street (Marstons) Yates's Bar, High Street (Yates) BowlPlex, The Atrium (BowlPlex)
Chobham		Car Park, off High Street
Frimley		Church Road Frimley Green Recreation Ground (Daytime) Frimley Lodge Park, Sturt Road (M&F)

Lightwater	⊘	Lightwater Country Park (Daytime)

SWALE

Boughton	⊘	The Street/School Lane (Mon-Sat, Daytime)
Faversham	⊘	Central Car Park Co-op Supermarket, South Road (Co-op) The Leading Light", Preston Street (JDW)
Leysdown-on-Sea	⊘	The Grove (Seasonal, Daytime) The Spinney, Leysdown Road
Minster	⊘	White House, the Broadway
Queenborough	⊘	Queenborough Park
Sheerness	⊘	Bridge Street Rose Street (Mon-Sat) Tesco Store, Bridge Road (Tesco)
Sittingbourne	⊘	Central Avenue The Forum (Mon-Sat) Sittingbourne Station (SE Rlwy) Asda Store (Asda) The Summoner, High Street (JDW)

TANDRIDGE

Bletchingley	⊘	Millers, High Street (Private)
Burstow	⊘	Shipley Bridge, Antlands Lane (Private)
Caterham	⊘	West Way/Chaldon Road Pilgrim, Godstone Road (Private)
Dormansland	⊘	Dormans High Street
Godstone	⊘	A22 Southbound Lay-by, Godstone Hill Godstone Green
Lingfield	⊘	Godstone Road/Jenny Lane
Oxted	⊘	A25 Westbound, Nags Hall lay-by

Ellice Road Car Park
Station Road West
Oxted Station (Southern)
Oxted Inn, Station Road West (JDW)

Warlingham	🔸	Leas Road/Westhall Road
Whyteleafe	🔸	Recreation Ground, Hillbury Road Station Road Car Park

THANET

Birchington	🔸	Alpha Road Car Park (Daytime) Minnis Bay Car Park (Daytime)
Broadstairs	🔸	Albion Road Car Park Clock Tower, Victoria Promenade (Daytime) Croft's Place Car Park (Daytime) Harbour (Daytime) Hopeville Avenue, St Peters (Daytime) Joss Bay (Summer, Daytime) Nandos, Westwood Cross (Nandos)
Margate	🔸	Buenos Ayres, Marine Terrace (Daytime) The Centre Shopping Mall (Daytime) College Walk (Daytime) Harold Road (Daytime) The Oval Bandstand West Bay Promenade Margate Station, Platform 1 (SE Rlwy) Margate Magistrates Court (Courts Service) Yates's Bar, Cecil Square (Yates)
Ramsgate	🔸	Bathing Station (Easter-September) Cavendish Street (Daytime) East Pier Yard, Harbour (Daytime) King George VI Memorial Park (Park hrs) Screaming Alley, off Grange Road (Daytime)
Westgate	🔸	St Mildred's Gap (Daytime) Station Road (Daytime)

TONBRIDGE & MALLING

Borough Green	🔸	High Street, Village Hall Car Park (6.00-18.00)

East Peckham ⊘ The Pound, Snoll Hatch Road (6.00-18.00)

Hadlow ⊘ Court Lane, A26 junction (6.00-18.00)
Two Brewers, Maidstone Road (Harveys)

Larkfield ⊘ Leybourne Country Park (Park hrs)
Martin Square

Snodland ⊘ Rockfort Road, Car Park (6.00-18.00)

Tonbridge ⊘ Angel Centre (6.00-18.00)
Castle Street (6.00-18.00)
Haysden Country Park (Park hrs)
Lamberts Yard, off High Street (6.00-18.00)
Priory Road
Racecourse Sports Ground (6.00-18.00)
Tonbridge Station, Platform 3 (SE Rlwy)
Humphrey Bean, High Street (JDW)
Vauxhall Inn, Vauxhall Lane (Private)

West Malling ⊘ King Street, off High Street
West Malling Station (SE Rlwy)

Wrotham ⊘ High Street (6.00-18.00)

TUNBRIDGE WELLS

Cranbrook ⊘ Crane Lane
White Horse, Carriers Road (Private)

Goudhurst ⊘ Balcombes Hill Car Park
Bedgebury National Pinetum (Forest Enterprise)

Paddock Wood ⊘ Commercial Road Car Park East
Paddock Wood Station (SE Rlwy)

Southborough ⊘ London Road, by Silk Restaurant
Pennington Grounds, Pennington Road

Sissinghurst ⊘ The Street (7.00-dusk)

Tunbridge Wells ⊘ Calverley Park (7.00-dusk)
Ca\mden Centre, Market Square (Centre hrs)
Crescent Rd Car Park/Monson Rd

(8.00-18.00, less Sundays)
Dunorlan Park (7.00-dusk)
Grosvenor Recreation Ground (7.00-dusk)
Hawkenbury Recreation Ground (7.00-dusk)
Kent & Sussex Cemetery (Cemetery hrs)
St John's Recreation Ground Pavilion (7.00-dusk)
Union House, nr. Pantiles (7.00-18.00)
Wellington Rocks, The Common   (7.00-dusk)
Corn Exchange, Pantiles (Private)
Royal Victoria Place, nr. Shopmobility (Private)
Sainsbury's Store, Linden Park Road (Sainsbury)
Tunbridge Wells Station (SE Rlwy)
Beau Nash, Mount Ephraim (Private)
Gourmet Burger Kitchen, Mount Pleasant Rd
(Private)
Opera House, Mount Pleasant Road (JDW)
Robin Hood, Sandhurst Road (Private)
Wagamama, Mount Pleasant Road (Private)

WAVERLEY

Bramley ⊙ Windrush Close

Cranleigh ⊙ Cricket Green, Guildford Road
Village Way Car Park

Farncombe ⊙ Broadwater Park, Summers Road
North Street

Waverley Borough Council

For more information on Public
Facilities and access at many
attractions, why not telephone for
more details before you travel?

Please telephone for all enquiries:

01483 523 405

www.waverley.gov.uk

Farnham	⊘	Central Car Park, Victoria Road
		Farnham Park Golf Club, Folly Hill
		Gostry Meadow, Union Road
		The Hart, West Street
		Farnham Station, Platform 1 (SW Trains)
Frensham	⊘	Frensham Great Pond Visitor Centre
Godalming	⊘	Crown Court, High Street
		Holloway Hill Pavilion, Busbridge Lane
		Meadrow
		Winkworth Arboretum, by tearoom (National Trust)
		Jack Phillips, High Street (JDW)
Haslemere	⊘	Haslemere Recreation Ground Pavilion
		High Street Car Park
		St Christophers Green, Weyhill [Closed at present]
		Swan Inn, High Street (JDW)
Tilford	⊘	Tilford Green
Witley	⊘	Witley Common Centre (National Trust)

WEALDEN

Alfriston	⊘	The Dene Car Park
		The Willows Car Park

Supporting the work of RADAR

For more information please contact us:-

Council Offices, Pine Grove,
Crowborough, East Sussex TN6 1DH
Telephone: **01892 602730**
Minicom: **01323 443331**
Fax: **01892 602733**
Email: **works@wealden.gov.uk**
Website: **www.wealden.gov.uk**

Wealden
District Council

Birling Gap	⟩	Car Park (National Trust)
Crowborough	⟩	Council Offices (Office hrs) Croft Road Car Park [Closed at present]
East Hoathly	⟩	Foresters Arms, South Street (Harveys)
Forest Row	⟩	Lower Road Car Park (8.00-18.00)
Hailsham	⟩	Council Offices (Office hrs) Vicarage Field (Mon-Sat 8.00-18.00) St Marys Walk (Private)
Heathfield	⟩	Station Road Car Park
Isfield	⟩	Halfway House, Rose Hill (Harveys)
Mayfield	⟩	South Street Car Park
Pevensey	⟩	Pevensey Castle Car Park
Pevensey Bay	⟩	Sea Road (8.00-18.00)
Polegate	⟩	High Street
Stone Cross	⟩	Glyndley Garden Centre (Private)
Uckfield	⟩	Luxford Field Car Park Tesco Store, Bell Farm Road (Tesco) Uckfield Bus Station (Private)
Wadhurst	⟩	Commemoration Hall, High St (8.00-18.00)
Willingdon	⟩	The Triangle, A22

WOKING

Byfleet	⟩	Recreation Ground, Stream Close (Daytime)
Horsell	⟩	Wheatsheaf Common, Chobham Rd (Daytime)
Knaphill	⟩	High Street (Daytime)
Mayford	⟩	Mayford Village Hall (Hall hrs) (Private)

Sheerwater	◎	Recreation Ground, Blackmore Cres (Daytime)
West Byfleet	◎	Lavender Road (Daytime)
Woking	◎	Addison Road (Daytime)
		Heathside Car Park (Daytime, Mon-Sat)
		Market Square (Daytime)
		Victoria Way Car Park (Daytime)
		Woking Station, Platforms 1 & 4/5 (SW Trains)
		Café Giardino, Wolsey Walk (Private)
		Herbert Wells, Chertsey Road (JDW)
		O'Neills, Crown Square (M&B)
		Rat & Parrot, Chertsey Road (Private)
		RSVP, Chertsey Road (Private)
		Station, Chertsey Road (Private)
		Wheatsheaf, Chobham Road (Private)
		Yates's Bar, Chobham Road (Yates)
		Gala Bingo, Church Street East (Gala)

WORTHING

Highdown	◎	Highdown Gardens, A259 (Daytime)
West Worthing	◎	George V Avenue, by Post Office (Daytime)
Worthing	◎	Beach House Grounds (Summer, Daytime)
		Beach House Park, Bowls Pavilion (Daytime)
		Buckingham Road (Daytime)
		Homefield Park (Summer, Daytime)
		Pier (Summer, Daytime)
		Promenade by Lido, (Daytime)
		Promenade, opp Dome (Daytime)
		Sea Lane Car Park (Café hrs)
		Victoria Park (Daytime)
		High Street MSCP (NCP)
		Worthing Station (Southern)
		Caffe Nero, South Street (Private)
		Sir Timothy Shelley, Chapel Road (JDW)
		Que Pasa, Chapel Road (Marstons)
		Yates's Bar, Chapel Road (Yates)
		Gala Bingo, Rowlands Road (Gala)

SOUTHERN ENGLAND

AYLESBURY VALE

Aston Clinton ❯ Duck Inn, London Road (Private)

Aylesbury ❯ Cemetery (Cemetery hrs)
Civic Centre MSCP [To Close Summer 09]
Friarscroft Car Park (8.30-19.30)
Upper Hundreds Car Park (7.30-19.30)
Vale Park (7.30-19.30)
Aylesbury Bus Station, Friars Square (Private)
Aylesbury Station, Platform 3 (Chiltern Railways)
Chicago Rock Café, Exchange Street (Private)
Cotton Wheel, Jasckson Road (Private)
The Harrow, Cambridge Street (Private)
Litten Tree, Kingsbury Court (Private)
New Zealand, Buckingham Road (Private)
Slug & Lettuce, Exchange Street (Private)
Weavers, Park Street (Private)
Yates's Bar, Exchange Street (Yates)

Bedgrove ❯ Buckinghamshire Yeoman, Cambourne Ave (Private)

Buckingham ❯ Moreton Road (7.30-22.00)
Swan Pool & Leisure Centre (Private)

Grove ❯ Grove Lock (Fullers)

Stoke Mandeville ❯ Bucks CC Sports & Social Club (Club hrs)

Swanbourne ❯ Betsey Wynne, Mursley Road (Private)

Waddesdon ❯ A41 Layby

Wendover ❯ Library Car Park (7.30-19.30)
Ellesborough Golf Club, Butlers Cross (Private)

Winslow ❯ Greyhound Lane, Car Park (8.00-17.00)

BASINGSTOKE & DEANE

Basingstoke ❯ Castons Yard, off New Road
New Road, by Red Lion Lane

Wortling Road Cemetery
Potter's Walk, opp. Library (Private)
Debenhams Store, Festival Pl (Debenhams)
Viables Craft Centre, Harrow Way (Private)
Basingstoke Station, Platforms 2/3 (SW Trains)
Lloyds Bar, Festival Place (JDW)
Maidenhead Inn, Winchester Street (JDW)
Nandos, Festival Place (Nandos)
Yates's Bar, London Street (Yates)
Gala Bingo, Basingstoke Leisure Pk. (Gala)

Eastrop ❯ Eastrop Park

Kempshott ❯ Old Down Close
Stratton Park, by Pavilion

Kingsclere ❯ Swan Street

Overton ❯ Winchester Street, Community Car Park

St Mary Bourne ❯ Bourne Meadow, opp. Village Hall

Tadley ❯ Mulfords Hill

Whitchurch ❯ Bell Street, Car Park

BOURNEMOUTH

Boscombe ❯ Ashley Road Bus Station
& Southbourne Boscombe Overcliff Gardens
Fisherman's Walk, Southbourne
Hengistbury Head, Double Dykes
Seabourne Road, opp Pokesdown Station
Southbourne Crossroads
Tuckton Road, nr Belle Vue Rd
Wick Lane Car Park, Tuckton
Sir Percy Florence Shelley,
Christchurch Rd (JDW)
Yates's Bar, Dean Park Crescent (Yates)

Bournemouth ❯ East Overcliffe, opp. Carlton Hotel
Firbank Road/Charminster Road (2)
Glen Fern Road Car Park
Lower Gardens, Exeter Crescent
Poole Hill, Ther Triangle
Richmond Gardens MSCP (Daytime)

Travel Interchange, by Coach Station
West Overcliffe, nr West Hill
Westover Road, by Information Bureau
Bournemouth Station, Platform 2/3 (SW Trains)
Debenhams Store, The Square (Debenhams)
Christopher Creeke, Holdenhurst Road (JDW)
Moon in the Square, Exeter Road (JDW)
Nandos, Castlepoint (Nandos)
Walkabout, Old Christchurch Rd (Private)

Kinson Green ❯ Milhams Road (Daytime)

Seafront ❯ Alum Chine, Bournemouth
Bedford Beach, Southbourne
Boscombe East
Boscombe West
Bournemouth East
Bournemouth Pier
Bournemouth West
Coasters, nr Boscombe Pier
Durley Chine, Bounemouth

Wallisdown ❯ Old Mulberry Close, Aldi car park

Westbourne ❯ Milburn Road Car Park

Winton ❯ Leslie Road
Parkstone & Heathlands, Wimborne Rd (JDW)
Gala Bingo, Wimborne Road (Gala)

BRACKNELL FOREST

Bracknell ❯ Birch Hill Shopping Parade
Brooke House, High Street
Bus Station
High Street MSCP, Level 4 (Daytime)
Old Manor, Church Road (JDW)

Crowthorne ❯ Napier Road

Warfield ❯ Shepherds House, Moss End (Private)

CHERWELL

Ardley M40 ❯ Cherwell Valley Services, J10 M40 (Moto)

Banbury	>	Bridge Street, by Town Hall (6.00-19.00)
		Bus Station
		Horsefair (6.00-19.00)
		Hardwick Hill Cemetery (Daytime) (Town Council)
		Southam Rd Cemetery (Daytime) (Town Council)
		Debenhams Store, Castle Quay (Debenhams)
		Banbury Station, upper level (Chiltern Railways)
		The Exchange, High Street (JDW)
		Fleur-de-Lis, Broad Street (JDW)
		Que Pasa, High Street (Marstons)
		Yates's Bar, Dean Park Crescent (Yates)

Bicester	>	Bure Place, Crown Car Park (6.00-19.00)
		Claremont (6.00-19.00)
		Litten Tree, Sheep Street (Private)
		Penny Black, Sheep Street (JDW)

Kidlington	>	Watts Way Car Park, off High St (6.00-19.00)

CHILTERN

Amersham on the Hill	>	Woodside Close, off Sycamore Rd (Daytime)
		Chalfont St GilesHigh Street (Daytime)

Chalfont St Peter	>	High Street

Chesham	>	Star Yard Car Park (Daytime)
		Lowndes Park (Town Council)

Cherwell

DISTRICT COUNCIL
North Oxfordshire

For more Information on Toilet
Facilities and Access at all Local
Attractions, why not telephone
for more details before you travel?

Please telephone for all enquiries:
01295 252535

Great Missenden	🔂	Link Road (Daytime)
Little Chalfont	🔂	Snells Wood Car Park (Daytime)
Old Amersham	🔂	Dovecote Meadow, Car Park (Daytime)
Prestwood	🔂	High Street, Car Park (Daytime)

CHRISTCHURCH

Christchurch	🔂	Bridge Street (8.00-20.00 or dusk) Christchurch Quay (8.00-20.00 or dusk) Kings Arms Bowls Pavilion (8.00-20.00 or dusk) Saxon Square, off High Street (8.00-18.00)
Friars Cliffe	🔂	Promenade, by Beach Café (Café hrs)
Highcliffe	🔂	Highcliffe Cliffe Top (Café hrs) Recreation Ground, Wharncliffe Rd (8.00-20.00 or dusk) Sea Corner, Waterford Road
Mudeford	🔂	Quay Head Recreation Ground, Ledbury Road (8.00-20.00 or dusk)
Mudeford Sandbank	🔂	Toilet Block 3, nr Ferry Pontoon Toilet Block 5, nr Black House (March-October)
Purewell	🔂	Purewell Cross Roads

EAST HAMPSHIRE

Alton	🔂	Lady Place Car Park (CP) Turk Street, Draymans Way
Bordon	🔂	Camp Road/High Street A325 The Forest Shopping Centre (Private)
Grayshott	🔂	Headley Road Car Park
Horndean	🔂	Blendworth Lane Car Park
Liphook	🔂	Parish Council Office, Midhurst Rd (Parish Council)

Liss ❯ Lower Mead Shops (Private)

Petersfield ❯ Central Car Park
St Peters Road
Ramswalk (2) (Private)
Petersfield Station, Platform 2 (SW Trains)

Selborne ❯ Car Park, behind Selborne Arms

EASTLEIGH

Bishopstoke ❯ Bishopstoke Road, Playing Fields

Botley ❯ Mortimer Road Car Park (Parish Council)

Chandlers Ford ❯ Winchester Road, The Precinct
Chandlers Ford Station, Booking Hall (SW Trains)

Eastleigh ❯ Bus Station Concourse
Mitchell Road MSCP, Southampton Road
Lakeside Park
Eastleigh Station, Booking Hall (SW Trains)
Nandos, Swan Centre (Nandos)
Wagon Works, Southampton Road (JDW)
AMF Bowl, Swan Centre (AMF)

Hamble ❯ Foreshore Car Park

Southern England

Hedge End	❯	Lower Northam Road (Town Council)
Netley	❯	Abbey Hall, Victoria Road Royal Victoria Country Park (Hants CC)
Southampton Airport	❯	Southampton Airport Station (SW Trains)
West End	❯	Itchen Valley Country Park Chapel Road (Parish Council)

FAREHAM

Fareham	❯	Trinity Street Fareham Shopping Centre, by Shopmobility (Private) Fareham Shopping Centre, Thackery Mall (Private) Crown Inn, West Street (JDW) Lord Arthur Lee, West Street (JDW)
Hill Head	❯	Meon Shore Salterns Lane Car Park
Locksheath	❯	Lockswood Centre
Park Gate	❯	Middle Road, by shops
Portchester	❯	Castle Street Car Park, by shops Waterside Lane, by Castle
Sarisbury	❯	Holly Hill Woodland Park
Stubbington	❯	Monks Hill Stubbington Green
Titchfield	❯	Barry's Meadow, Southampton Hill
Warsash	❯	Passage Lane

GOSPORT

Gosport	❯	Falkland Gardens Forton Recreation Ground [Temp. closed] Jamaica Place Nobes Avenue [Temp. closed]

Ordnance Road
The Star, High Street (JDW)

Lee-on-Solent ❯ Marine Parade Central, Car Park
Marine Parade East
Marine Parade West

Stokes Bay ❯ Central
Gilkicker
No. 2 Battery

HART

Eversley Cross ❯ Frog & Wicket (Private) [to be fitted]

Fleet ❯ Church Road Car Park
The Fleet Centre (Private)
Fleet Station, Platform 2 (SW Trains)
Prince Arthur, Fleet Road (JDW)

Hartley Wintney ❯ Car Park, off High Street

Hook ❯ Car Park, London Road A30

Odiham ❯ Waterwitch, Colthill (Private)

HAVANT

Bedhampton ❯ Bidbury Mead Recreation Ground

Cowplain ❯ Mission Lane Car Park
Recreation Ground, Padnell Avenue

Emsworth ❯ Recreation Ground, Horndean Road
South Street Car Park

Havant ❯ Civic Offices
Havant Park, Havant Parade
Staunton Country Park (Hants CC)
Meridian Centre, nr. Library (Private)
Havant Bus Station, Elm Lane (Private)
Havant Station, Platform 1 (SW Trains)
Parchment Makers, Park Rd North (JDW)

Hayling Island ❯ Bosmere Road (Summer only)

Central Beachlands
Chichester Avenue
Eastoke Corner
Elm Grove
Ferry Point
Nab Tower Car Park
Station Road
West Beachlands Car Park

Langstone ❯ Ship Inn

Leigh Park ❯ Greywell Car Park

Purbrook ❯ Purbrook Heath Recreation Ground

Warblington ❯ Warblington Cemetery (Cemetery hrs)

Waterlooville ❯ Swiss Road
Waterlooville Cemetery (Cemetery hrs)
Woodpecker, London Road (Private)

ISLE OF WIGHT

Bembridge ❯ Harold Lewis Day Centre, High Street
Lane End
Whitecliff Bay Holiday Park (2) (Private)

Binstead ❯ Recreation Ground, Binstead Hill

Brighstone ❯ Warnes Lane Car Park

Carisbrooke ❯ High Street Car Park (Daytime)

Colwell ❯ Colwell Chine Road Car Park

Compton Bay ❯ Military Road Car Park (April-Oct)

Cowes, East ❯ Albany Road (April-Oct)
Osbourne Road, by Town Hall
Car Ferry Terminal (Red Funnel)

Cowes, West ❯ Cowes Parade
Cross Street, off High Street
Medina Road
Mornington Road (April-Oct)

Park Road Car Park
Passenger Ferry Terminal (Red Funnel)

Godshill ❯ Car Park, High Street

Gurnard ❯ Shore Road

Lake ❯ New Road/High Street (Daytime)

Newport ❯ Church Litten, South Street Car Park
Post Office Lane
Sea Close Park
William Coppin, Coppins Bridge (JDW)

Ryde ❯ Appley Park, Garden Walk
Eastern Esplanade (April-Oct)
Puckpool Park
St Johns Road
Town Hall, Lind Street
Western Esplanade, The Pier
S Fowler & Co, Union Street (JDW)

St Helens ❯ The Duver (May-September)
St Helens Green

Sandown ❯ Battery Gardens (Apr-October)
Eastern Gardens (Daytime)
Pier Street (M&F) (Daytime)
St John's Road Car Park (Daytime)

Seaview ❯ Ropewalk (Private)

Shanklin ❯ The Esplanade (Daytime)
Falcon Cross Road (M&F)
Lake Cliff Gardens, Skew Bridge (Apr-Oct)
Tower Cottage Gardens (Daytime)
Shanklin Station, Platform (Island Line)

Ventnor ❯ Botanic Gardens, Visitor Centre (Centre hrs)
Eastern Esplanade (M&F) (Daytime)
Marlborough Road (M&F) (Daytime)
Pound Lane

Wootton ❯ Car Park, off Brannon Way

Yarmouth ❯ Bridge Road

High Street, opp. Common (April-Oct)

Yaverland ❯ Culver Parade Car Park

MILTON KEYNES

Bletchley ❯ Albert Street (Neighbourhood Council)
George Street (Neighbourhood Council)
Bletchley Station, Booking Hall (London Midland)

Caldecotte ❯ Caldecotte Arms, Bletchern Way (Private)

Milton Keynes Central ❯ the centre:mk (Private) CP
John Lewis Store (John Lewis)
Milton Keynes Station (London Midland)
City Limits, Xscape Village (Private)
Ha! Ha! Bar, Midsummer Boulevard (Private)
Lloyds Bar, Theatre Quarter (JDW)
Nandos, The Hub (Nandos)
Nandos Xscape (Nandos)
Moon Under Water, Avebury Boulevard (JDW)
Rat & Parrot, Theatre Quarter (Private)
Secklow Hundred, Midsummer Boulevard (JDW)
Wetherspoons, Bouverie Square (JDW)

Newport Pagnell ❯ Market Hill (Town Council)

Olney ❯ Market Square (Town Council)

Stoney Stratford ❯ Silver Street (Neighbourhood Council)

Wolverton ❯ Wolverton Station (London Midland)

Wroughton-on ❯ Ye Old Swan, Newport Road (Private)
-the-Green

NEW FOREST DISTRICT COUNCIL

Barton-on-Sea ❯ Barton Court Avenue/Marine Drive

Beaulieu ❯ Car Park, Palace Lane

Blackfield ❯ Lepe Country Park (Hants CC)

Bransgore ❯ Betsy Lane Car Park

New Forest Caravan Club Site (Caravan Club)

Brockenhurst ❯ Fibbards Road Car Park
Black Knowl Caravan Club Site (Caravan Club)

Burley ❯ Chapel Lane Car Park

Calshot ❯ Calshot Spit

Fawley ❯ Car Park

Fordingbridge ❯ Roundhill Car Park
Sandy Balls Holiday Park (Private)

Hythe ❯ Hythe Pier

Keyhaven ❯ Car Park

Lymington ❯ Bath Road Car Park
New Street
Powlett Road, M&S Car Park
Quay Road

Lyndhurst ❯ Car Park, High Street (2)

Milford-on-Sea ❯ Hordle Cliff Car Park
Hurst Road, Car Park
Sea Road, Car Park

New Milton ❯ Recreation Ground, Old Milton Road
Station Road, Car Park

Ringwood ❯ Ringwood Furlong Car Park

Totton ❯ Cemetery Car Park, Eling Hill
Eling Recreation Ground, Bartram Road
Library Road
Winsor Road

OXFORD

Oxford ❯ Abingdon Road, Hinksey Park
Barns Road, Cowley
Bury Knowle Park, Headington
Castle Street
Cowley Road

Diamond Place, Summertown
Gloucester Green Bus Station
Market Street
Oxpens Coach Park
St Clements
Speedwell Street
Westgate Car Park, Level 4
Oxford Station, Concourse (Gt Western)
Botanic Garden, Rose Lane (Private)
Debenhams Store, Magdalen St (Debenhams)
Four Candles, George Street (JDW)
Ha! Ha! Bar, Oxford Castle (Private)
Jongleurs, Hythe Bridge Road (Private)
Nandos, Cowley Road (Nandos)
Old Orleans, George Street (Private)
Swan & Castle, Castle Street (JDW)
The Victoria, 90 Walton Street (Private)
William Morris, Cowley (JDW)
Yates's Bar, George Street (Yates)

POOLE

Branksome ❯
Branksome Chine, Beach Car Park
Branksome Dene Chine
Branksome Recreation Ground
Poole Road [Closed at present]

Broadstone ❯
Macaulay Road

Canford Heath ❯
The Pilot Car Park. Adastral Road
Haymoor Bottom Shopping Centre (Private)

Hamworthy ❯
Ashmore Avenue, Hamworthy Park
Blandford Road, by Co-op
Lake Pier, Lake Drive (8.00-18.00, longer in Summer)

Holton Heath ❯
Sandford Holiday Park (Private)

Parkstone ❯
Alexandra Park Recreation Ground
Jubilee Road
Viewpoint, Constitution Hill

Poole ❯
Chapel Lane [Closed at present]
Haven Ferry, Panorama Road
Kingland Road Bus Station
Newfoundland Drive, Baiter Park

Poole Park, Central Park Café
Poole Park, West Gate (8.00-18.00)
Whitecliff Recreation Ground
Dolphin Square (Private)
Lord Wimborne, Lagland Street (JDW)
Nandos, Tower Park (Nandos)
Yates's Bar, High Street (Yates)
BowlPlex, Tower Park (BowlPlex)

The Quay ❯ Quay Visitors Centre
Watch Station, nr Lifting Bridge
Dolphin Quays (Private)
The Quay, The Quay (JDW)

Sandbanks ❯ Banks Road, Sandbanks Pavilion
Shore Road, Beach Pavilion

Upton Country Park ❯ Upton Heritage Centre (8.00-18.00, longer in Summer)

❯ Upton Park Car Park (8.00-18.00, longer in Summer)

PORTSMOUTH

Cosham ❯ Wootton Street
The First Post, High Street (JDW)

Fratton ❯ Clarkes Road (7.00-16.30)
Asda Store, Fratton (Asda)

Hilsea ❯ Hilsea Lido

North End ❯ Sir John Baker, London Road (JDW)

Paulsgrove ❯ Marsden Road

Portsmouth ❯ Bransbury Park (7.00-19.00)
Buckland Park
College Park
Derby Road
Guildhall Square (8.00-17.00)
The Hard Interchange
Milton Park (7.00-17.00)
Paradise Street (7.00-19.00)
Point Battery
Victoria Park (Park hrs)

White Hart Road
Morrisons Store, Anchorage Road (Morrison)
Portsmouth & Southsea Station, Concourse
(SW Trains)
Portsmouth Harbour Station, Concourse
(SW Trains)
Bar 38, Gun Wharf Quays (Private)
Ha! Ha! Bar, Gun Wharf Quays (Private)
Isambard Kingdom Brunel, Guildhall Walk (JDW)
John Jacques, Fratton Road (JDW)
Jongleurs, Gun Wharf Quays (Private)
Lloyds Bar, The Boardwalk (JDW)
Nandos, Gunwharf Quays (Nandos)
Trafalgar, Edinburgh Road (JDW)
Walkabout, Guildhall Walk (Private)
White Swan, Guildhall Walk (JDW)
Yates's Bar, High Street (Yates)

Southsea ❯

Albert Road
Canoe Lake
Castlefield
Clarence Pier
D-Day Museum Car Park (April-Sept)
Eastney Esplanade
Highland Road
Pyramids (April-September)
Richmond Place
St Georges Road
South Parade Kiosk (April-September)

READING

Burghfield M4 ❯ Reading East Services, M4 Juncts 11-12 (Moto)

Caversham ❯ St Martins Precinct, by Waitrose
Baron Cadogan, Prospect Street (JDW)

Reading ❯

Blagrave Street
Broad Street Mall
Cemetery Junction
Cintra Park Pavilion
Friars Walk
Honey End Lane
Hosier Street, nr. Market
Meadway Precinct
Old Market Place

Oxford Road/Wilson Road
Queens Road Car Park
Thame Side Promenade, Richfield Avenue
Debenhams, The Oracle (Debenhams)
Reading Station, Concourse & Platform 4
(Gt Western)
Back of Beyond, Kings Road (JDW)
Bar 12, Station Road (Private)
Bar 38, Oracle Centre (Private)
Ha! Ha! Bar, Kings Road (Private)
The Hope Tap, Friar Street (JDW)
Jongleurs, Friar Street (Private)
Monks Retreat, Friar Street (JDW)
Nandos, Riverside, The Oracle (Nandos)
Old Orleans, The Oracle (Private)
Nandos, Friar Street (Nandos)
O'Neill's, Blagrave Street (M&B)
Pavlov's Dog. St Mary's Butts (Private)
Slug & Lettuce, The Oracle (Private)
Varsity, Friar Street (Barracuda)
Walkabout, Wiston Terrace (Private)
Yates's Bar, Friar Street (Yates)

Southcote ❯ Prospect Park, Tilehurst Road

Tilehurst ❯ Kentwood Hill, by the Whitehouse
The Bear, Park Lane (Private)

Whitley ❯ Northumberland Avenue
Whitley Street
Whitley Wood Pavilion, Acre Road

RUSHMOOR

Aldershot ❯ Aldershot Park, Guildford Road
Manor Park, High Street/Ash Road
Princes Gardens, High Street
Wellington Centre (Private)
Aldershot Bus Station (Private)
Aldershot Station, Platform 1 (SW Trains)
Yates's Bar, Victoria Road (Yates)

Farnborough ❯ King George V Playing Fields Pavilion (Daytime)
Princes Mead (Private)
Farnborough Main Station, Platform 2 (SW Trains)

North Camp ❯ High Street

SLOUGH

Langley ❯ East Berkshire College (College)
Langley Station (Gt Western)

Slough ❯ Brunel Bus Station
The Grove, Slough High Street
Station Approach
Observatory Shopping Centre (2) (Private)
Queensmere Centre (Private)
Slough Station, Platform 2 (Gt Western)
The Moon & Spoon, High Street (JDW)
Newt & Cucumber, High Street (Private)

SOUTHAMPTON

Bitterne ❯ Bitterne Triangle, Cobden Bridge
Maytree Road, Bitterne Precinct

Lordshill ❯ Gala Bingo, Lordshill Retail Park (Gala)

Portswood ❯ Westridge Road

Shirley ❯ Bright Water Inn, 370 Shirley Road (JDW)
Malvern Tavern, Winchester Road (Private)

Southampton ❯ Bargate Street

City Centre ❯ East Park Pavilion (Daytime)
Kingsland Square, St Marys Square
Mayflower Park
Poundtree Road
The Mall Marlands Shopping Centre (Private)
Debenhams Store, Queensway (Debenhams)
Southampton Central Station, Platforms 1 & 4
(SW Trains)
Admiral Sir Lucius Curtis, Ocean Village (JDW)
Giddy Bridge London Road (JDW)
Jongleurs, Bargate (Private)
Que Pasa, Above Bar Street (Marstons)
Standing Order, High Street (JDW)
Varsity, London Road (Barracuda)
Walkabout, High Street (Private)
Yates's Bar, Above Bar Street (Yates)

| Weston | ❯ | Mayfield Park |
| | | Weston Shore, Car Park |

SOUTH BUCKS

Beaconsfield	❯	Windsor End, Old Town (Town Council)
Burnham	❯	Jennery Lane Car Park (Parish Council)
Denham	❯	Wyatts Covert Caravan Site (Caravan Club)
Farnham Common	❯	Beaconsfield Road Car Park (Parish Council)
		Royal Oak, Beaconsfield Road (Private)
Iver	❯	Iver Garden Centre (Private)

SOUTH OXFORDSHIRE

Didcot	❯	Orchard Centre (Private)
		Didcot Parkway Station, Platform 2 (Gt Western)
Dorchester	❯	Bridge End
Goring	❯	Car Park off Station Road
Henley-on-Thames	❯	Greys Road Car Park
		Kings Road Car Park
		Station Road
		Mill Meadows, Mill Road (Town Council)
		Catherine Wheel", Hart Street (JDW)
		Four Oaks Caravan Club Site (Caravan Club)
Thame	❯	Market House
		North Street
Wallingford	❯	Cattlemarket Car Park, Wood Street
		Riverside (April-October)
		St Albans Car Park
Watlington	❯	Church Street (Parish Council)

TEST VALLEY

| Andover | ❯ | Borden Gate Car Park (Mon-Sat, 8.00-18.00) |
| | | Chantry Centre, by MSCP |

George Yard Car Park (Mon-Sat, 8.00-6.00)
John Russell Fox, High Street (JDW)

Ower   **❯**   Vine Inn, Romsey Road (Private)

Romsey   **❯**   Bus Station Car Park, Broadwater Road

Stockbridge   **❯**   High Street (8.00-18.00) (Parish Council)

VALE OF WHITE HORSE

Abingdon   **❯**   Abbey Meadow (Daytime, April-September)
Charter MSCP (Daytime)
Hales Meadow Car Park

Botley   **❯**   Elms Court, Chapel Way, A35 (Daytime)

Faringdon   **❯**   Southampton Street Car Park (Daytime)

Wantage   **❯**   Manor Recreation Ground (Daytime)
Portway Car Park (Daytime)

WEST BERKSHIRE

Aldermaston   **❯**   The Wharf (8.00-18.00 Apr-Sept)

Hungerford   **❯**   Church Street (8.00-18.00)

West Berkshire
COUNCIL

All Public Conveniences under our control have
RADAR keys.
They are normally open between 0800 – 1800 daily.

Keys are available from the Market Street,
Council Offices for a small fee.

For locations or further information
please contact 01635 42400.
You can also visit our website www.westberks.gov.uk
or West Berkshire Disability Alliance website
www.wbda.org for further information.

Kintbury	❯	Station Road (8.00-18.00)
Lambourn	❯	Community Centre (Parish Council)
Newbury	❯	Parkway (8.00-18.00) Pembroke Road MSCP (8.00-18.00) The Wharf (8.00-18.00) Snelsmore Common Country Park (Daytime) Kennet Shopping (Private) Weavers Walk (Private) Newbury Station, Platform (Gt Western) Sainsbury's Store, Hector Way (Sainsbury) Lock Stock & Barrel, Northbrook St (Fullers) Vue Cinema (Private)
Pangbourne	❯	River Meadow (April-September, 8.00-18.00) Station Road (8.00-18.00)
Thatcham	❯	Broadway (8.00-18.00) The Kingsland Centre (Private)

WEST OXFORDSHIRE

Bampton	❯	Town Hall, Market Square
Burford	❯	High Street Guildenford Car Park [Closed at present] Burford Caravan Site (Caravan Club)
Carterton	❯	Black Bourton Road, Car Park
Charlbury	❯	Spendlove Centre (Daytime)
Chipping Norton	❯	New Street, Car Park Town Hall, Market Place
Eynsham	❯	Back Lane Car Park [Closed at present] Oxford Road Playing Field
Witney	❯	Langdale Gate The Leys (Daytime) Welch Way, Car Park
Woodstock	❯	Browns Lane Hensington Road Car Park Bladon Chains Caravan Site (Caravan Club)

WINCHESTER

Bishops Waltham ❯ Central Car Park, Houchin Street

Denmead ❯ Kidmore Lane Car Park

New Alresford ❯ Station Road

Wickham ❯ Station Road
Rooksbury Park Caravan Club Site
(Caravan Club)

Winchester ❯ Abbey Gardens
Chesil Street MSCP
Jewry Street
Market Lane
Middle Brook Street
St Catherines Park & Ride (daytime)
Tower Street Car Park
Worthy Lane Coach Station/Car Park
Brooks Shopping Centre (Private)
Debenhams Store, High Street (Debenhams)
Winchester Station, Platform 2 (SW Trains)
Bishop on the Bridge, High Street (Fullers)
Old Gaol House, Jewry Street (JDW)
Morn Hill Caravan Club Site (Caravan Club)

WINDSOR & MAIDENHEAD

Ascot ❯ Station Hill
Ascot Station, Platform 1 (SW Trains)

Cookham ❯ Sutton Road Car Park

Eton ❯ Eton Court Car Park

Hurley ❯ Hurley Riverside Park (Private)

Maidenhead ❯ Broadway MSCP (7.30-18.00)
Providence Place (8.00-18.00)
Magnet Leisure Centre (CP)
Bear, High Street (Private)
Greyhound, Queen Street (JDW)

Sunninghill ❯ High Street

Windsor ❯ Coach Park (Daytime)
River Street Car Park
Windsor Leisure Centre (Centre hrs)
East Berkshire College (College)
Windsor & Eton Riverside Station, Concourse
Ha! Ha! Bar, Windsor Royal Station (Private)
King & Castle, Thames Street (JDW)
Nandos, 10 Thames Street (Nandos)
Windlesora, William Street (JDW)

WOKINGHAM

Barkham ❯ Ye Olde Leathern Bottle, Barkham Rd (Private)

Twyford ❯ Twyford Station, Platform (Gt Western)

Wokingham ❯ Gig House, Denmark Street (JDW)
Gala Bingo, Easthampstead Road (Gala)

WYCOMBE

Bourne End ❯ Wakeman Road

Flackwell Heath ❯ Straight Bit

Hambleden ❯ Mill End Car Park

Hazlemere ❯ Beaumont Way
Park Parade

High Wycombe ❯ Easton Street MSCP
Pauls Row (Daytime)
Sainsburys Dovecote MSCP (Daytime)
Eden Shopping Centre (Private)
The Falcon, Cornmarket (JDW)
Nandos, Eden Shopping Centre (Nandos)
William Robert Loosley, Oxford Road (JDW)
AMF Bowl, Eden Centre (AMF)

Marlow ❯ Central Car Park, Crown Lane
Pound Lane (Daytime)
Marlow Library (Library hrs) (Bucks CC)

Princes Risborough ❯ Horns Lane Car Park

West Wycombe ❯ Hill Road

WEST COUNTRY

BATH & NORTH EAST SOMERSET

Bath City Centre

Charlotte Street Car Park
Charlotte Street, entrance to car park
Henrietta Park, Henrietta Street
Parade Gardens, Grand Parade
Riverside Coach Park, Avon Street
Royal Victoria Park, Pavilion, Royal Avenue
Royal Victoria Park, Play Area, Upper Bristol Rd
Seven Dials, Monmouth Street
Sydney Gardens, Sydney Place
Victoria Art Gallery (Gallery hrs)
Weston High Street, near shops
Podium Shopping Centre (Private)
Bath Spa Station, Platforms (Gt Western)
Bear, Wellsway (Private)
Ha! Ha! Bar, Walcot Street (Private)
King of Wessex, James Street (JDW)
Nandos, James Street West (Nandos)
Gala Bingo, Sawclose (Gala)
Newbridge Caravan Park (Private)

Bath, Beechen Cliff ❯   Alexandra Park, Shakespeare Avenue

Bath, Combe Down ❯   Bradford Road

Bath & North East Somerset Council

Council Connect
01225 39 40 41
www.bathnes.gov.uk

Bath, Lambridge	❯	Alice Park, Gloucester Road Larkhall Square
Bath, Lansdown	❯	Approach Golf Course, Weston Road
Bath, Odd Down	❯	Park & Ride Site
Bath, Oldfield Park	❯	Monksdale Road Shaftesbury Road
Bath, Twerton	❯	Twerton High Street, by stadium
Batheaston	❯	London Road Car Park (Parish Council)
Keynsham	❯	Ashton Way Car Park Memorial Park
Midsomer Norton	❯	Gullock Tyning, by Sports Centre The Island, High Street
Paulton	❯	High Street, Red Lion Car Park (Parish Council)
Peasedown St John	❯	Greenlands Road, car park
Saltford	❯	The Shallows Car Park, picnic area

BRISTOL

Ashton	❯	Ashton Road
Bedminster	❯	Bridgwater Road, Bedminster Down (Daytime) East Street Victoria Park (Park hrs) Robert Fitzharding, Cannon St. (JDW)
Brislington	❯	White Hart, Brislington Hill (Private)
Bristol City Centre	❯	Albion Marina, Hotwells (Daytime) Castle Park, Broadweir (Daytime) Colston Avenue (8.00-19.00) St James Barton (Daytime) Wapping Wharf, Redcliff (Daytime) The Mall Bristol, Broadmead, (3) (Private) Bristol Temple Meads Station (3) (Gt Western)

Bay Horse, Lewind Mead (Private)
Commercial Rooms, Corn Street (JDW)
Green House, College Green (Private)
Jongleurs, Baldwin Street (Private)
Knights Templar, Temple Quay (JDW)
Nandos, Cabot Circus (Nandos)
Que Pasa, Corn Street (Marstons)
V-Shed, The Waterfront (JDW)
Walkabout, Corn Street (Private)
Blue Wharf Aquarium, Anchor Road (Private)
Baltic Wharf Caravan Site (Caravan Club)

Clifton ❯ Central Museum, Queens Road (Museum hrs)
The Berkeley, Queens Road (JDW)
The Cotham Hill, Cotham Hill (Private)
Ha! Ha! Bar, Berkeley Square (Private)

Fishponds ❯ Fishponds Park (Daytime)
Van Dyke Forum", Fishponds Road (JDW)
Gala Bingo, Fishponds Road (Gala)

Knowle ❯ Redcatch Park (Park hrs)

Montpellier ❯ St Andrews Park (Park hrs)

Redfield ❯ St George's Hall, Church Road (JDW)

Southmead ❯ Greystoke Avenue (Daytime)

Stoke Bishop ❯ Sea Wall, Durdham Down (Daytime)
Stoke Road, by Water Tower (Daytime)

CHELTENHAM

Cheltenham ❯ Ambrose Street/High Street
Bath Terrace, off Bath Road
Coronation Square, Car Park
Cox's Meadow, Old Bath Road
Imperial Square, by Town Hall
Montpellier Gardens
Pittville Park
Royal Well Bus Station
Royal Well Road, by Municipal Offices
Beechwood Shopping Centre (Private)
Sainsbury's Store, Tewkesbury Rd (Sainsbury)
Cheltenham Spa Station (Gt Western)

Bank House, Clarence Street (JDW)
Ha! Ha! Bar, Montpellier Walk (Private)
Moon Under Water, Bath Road (JDW)
Nandos, St Margarets Road (Nandos)
Que Pasa, Clarence St (Marstons)
Yates's Bar, Crescent Terrace (Yates)

COTSWOLD

Bibury ❯ London Road (Daytime)

Bourton-on-the-Water ❯ Church Rooms (Daytime)
Rissington Road Car Park (Daytime)

Chipping Campden ❯ Sheep Street (Daytime)

Cirencester ❯ Brewery Car Park (Daytime)
Forum Car Park (Daytime)
London Road (Daytime)
Lorry Park (Daytime)
Abbey Grounds (April-Oct) (Town Council)
Cirencester Park Caravan Club Site
(Caravan Club)

Fairford ❯ High Street (Daytime)

Lechlade ❯ Burford Road (Daytime)

Moreton-in-Marsh ❯ High Street (Daytime)
Moreton-in-Marsh Caravan Club Site
(Caravan Club)

Northleach ❯ Market Place (Daytime)

Stow-on-the-Wold ❯ Market Square (Daytime)
Maugersbury Road Car Park (8.00-21.00)

Tetbury ❯ Chipping Street (Daytime)
West Street (Daytime)

EAST DORSET

Astley Heath ❯ Moors Valley Country Park (CP)

Corfe Mullen ❯ Towers Way

Ferndown	❯	Pennys Walk
		The Night Jar, Victoria Road (JDW)
Verwood	❯	Ferret Green
West Moors	❯	Park Way
West Parley	❯	Christchurch Road

FOREST OF DEAN

Blakeney	❯	High Street
Broomsgreen	❯	Memorial Hall (Hall Committee)
Cinderford	❯	Heywood Road
Coleford	❯	Railway Drive
Drybrook	❯	High Street
Dymock	❯	Ledbury Road
Littledean	❯	Silver Street
Lydbrook	❯	New Road
Lydney	❯	Newerne Street car park
Mitcheldean	❯	High Street car park
Newent	❯	Lewell Street, High Street
		Watery Lane
Newnham-on-Severn	❯	Riverside car park
Symonds Yat	❯	Car Park (Forest Enterprise)
Woolaston	❯	Peters Cross Picnic Area

GLOUCESTER

Gloucester	❯	Berkeley Street

Gloucester Bus Station
Gloucester Park (Park hrs)
Kings Square
Westgate Car Park
East Gate Shopping Chambers (Private)
Debenhams Store, Kings Sq (Debenhams)
Water Poet, Eastgate Street (JDW)
The Regal, Kings Square (JDW)
Sloans, Brunswick Road (Private)
Gala Bingo, Peel Centre (Gala)

Kingsholm ❯ Javelin Park & Ride (County Council)

Matson ❯ Robinswood Country Park

Quedgeley ❯ Waterwells Park & Ride (County Council)

MENDIP

Frome ❯ Market Yard Car Park, Justice Lane
Merchants Barton (Town Council)
Victoria Park, Weymouth Rd (Town Council)
Frome Station, Platform (Gt Western)

Glastonbury ❯ St John's Car Park
Magdalene Street (Town Council)

Shepton Mallet ❯ Commercial Road Car Park
Collett Park, Park Road   (Town Council)

Street ❯ Southside Car Park
Clarks Village (2) (Private)
The Lantokay, High Street (JDW)

Wells ❯ Union Street Car Park
Princes Road Car Park (Town Council)
Recreation Ground, Silver St (Town Council)
Kings Head, High Street (Private)

NORTH DORSET

Blandford Forum ❯ Marsh & Ham Car Park (Town Council)
Corn Exchange (Centre hrs) (Town Council)

Gillingham	❯	High Street Car Park (Town Council)
Shaftesbury	❯	Bell Street Car Park (Town Council)
Stalbridge	❯	Station Road Car Park (Town Council)
Sturminster Newton	❯	Station Road Car Park (Town Council)

NORTH SOMERSET

Clevedon	❯	Chalet Conveniences, Seafront
		Station Road
		Crab Apple Inn, Southern Way (Private)
Portishead	❯	Lake Grounds, Esplanade Rd (8.00-20.00)
		Wyndham Way Car Park
Uphill	❯	Links Road
Weston-super-Mare	❯	Boulevard, by Library (8.00-19.45)
		Grove Park Car Park (8.00-18.00)
		Locking Road 4 Car Park (8.00-20.00)
		Marine Parade, opp. Grand Atlantic Hotel
		Marine Parade, Oxford Street
		Marine Parade, Richmond St (Summer)
		Marine Parade, Sanatorium
		Rozel Seafront (8.00-20.00)
		Sand Bay Bus Terminal
		Weston-super-Mare Station (Gt Western)
		Dragon Inn, Meadow Street (JDW)
		Yates's Bar, Regent Street (Yates)
		Country View Caravan Park (Private)
Winscombe	❯	Woodborough Road
Worle	❯	The Maltings, High Street

PURBECK

Corfe Castle	❯	West Street
		Castle Ticket Office (National Trust)
Norden	❯	Park & Ride Car Park (Swanage Rlwy)
Studland	❯	Beach Road

Knoll Car Park (National Trust)
Middle Beach (National Trust)
Shell Bay (National Trust)

Swanage ⊘ Burlington Chine (Town Council)
Heritage Centre (Daytime) (Town Council)
Herston (Town Council)
Shore Road (Town Council)
Haycraft Caravan Club Site (Caravan Club)

Wareham ⊘ Howards Lane
Hunters Moon Caravan Club Site (Caravan Club)

Worth Maltravers ⊘ Car Park

SEDGEMOOR

Axbridge ⊘ Moorland Street (Daytime)

Berrow ⊘ Coast Road (Daytime)
Hurn Lane Caravan Club Site (Caravan Club)

Brean ⊘ South Road (Daytime)
Brean Leisure Park (Private)

Bridgwater ⊘ Blake Gardens (Mon-Sat, Daytime)
Coach Station, East Quay (Daytime)
Penel Orlieu
Taunton Road (Daytime)
Angel Place Shopping Centre (Private)
Carnival Inn, St Mary Street (JDW)

Bridgwater M5 ⊘ Bridgwater Services, J24 M5 (Moto)

Burnham-on-Sea ⊘ Apex Park (Daytime)
Crosses Penn, Manor Gardens (Daytime)
Oxford Street Car Park (Daytime)
South Esplanade, Information Centre (Daytime)
The Railway, College Street (Private)
Reeds Arms, Pier Street (JDW)

Cheddar ⊘ Cliff Street Car Park (Daytime)
Dagshole (Daytime)
Station Road, by School   (Daytime)
Cheddar Caravan Club Site (Caravan Club)

Highbridge	❯	Bank Street Car Park (Daytime)
Nether Stowey	❯	Castle Street, Library Car Park (Daytime)
North Petherton		Fore Street, A38 (Daytime)

SOUTH GLOUCESTERSHIRE

Alveston	❯	Ship Inn, Thornbury Road (Private)
Aust M48	❯	Severn View Services, J1 M48 (Moto)
Charfield	❯	Memorial Hall
Chipping Sodbury	❯	Wickwar Road, Car Park
Cribbs Causeway	❯	Nandos, Unit 208 Cribbs Causeway (Nandos)
Downend	❯	Westerleigh Road
Filton	❯	Church Road
Hanham	❯	Conham River Park Laburnham Road, Car Park Nandos, Aspect Leisure Park (Nandos)
Kingswood	❯	Kingswood Park, High Street

SOUTH SOMERSET DISTRICT COUNCIL

. . . contributing towards an overall improvement in physical and mental wellbeing

Moravian Road (M&F)
Kingschase Shopping Centre (Private)
Kingswood Colliers, Regent Street (JDW)

Mangotsfield ❯ St James Street Car Park (M&F)

Severn Beach ❯ Beach Road

Staple Hill ❯ Page Park
Page Road (M&F) (7.30-19.00)
Staple Hill Oak, High Street (JDW)

Stoke Gifford ❯ Bristol Parkway Station (2) (Gt Western)

Thornbury ❯ St Marys Shopping Centre (Private)
White Lion, High Street (Private)

Warmley ❯ Station Yard, High Street
Wick ❯ Golden Valley Shopping Centre (Private)

Winterbourne ❯ Flaxpits Lane

Yate ❯ Yate Shopping Centre (Private)

SOUTH SOMERSET

Bruton ❯ Grove Alley (Daytime)

Castle Cary ❯ Millbrook Gardens Car Park (Daytime)
Castle Cary Station (Gt Western)

Chard ❯ Bath Street (Daytime)
Boden Street (Daytime)
The Cerdic, Fore Street (JDW)
Five Acres Caravan Club Site (Caravan Club)

Crewkerne ❯ South Street

Ilchester ❯ Free Street

Ilminster ❯ Shudrick Lane (Daytime)

Langport ❯ Whatley Car Park (7.00-19.00)

Martock ❯ Market House, Church Street (Parish Council)

Milbourne Port	❱	London Road
Somerton	❱	West Street Car Park (Town Council)
South Petherton	❱	Prigg Lane (Daytime)
Stoke-sub-Hamdon	❱	Ham Hill (7.00-16.30, later in Summer) West Street (Daytime)
Wincanton	❱	Memorial Hall Car Park (7.00-19.00) Carrington Way (Town Council) Churchfields (Town Council) Wincanton Racecourse Caravan Site (Caravan Club)
Yeovil	❱	Bus Station, Earle Street (7.00-19.00) Petters Way Car Park (7.00-19.00) Recreation Ground, Mudford Road (7.00-19.00) Peter Street (Town Council) Quedam Centre (Mon-Sat Daytime) (Private) William Dampier, Middle Street (JDW)

STROUD

Berkeley	❱	Marybrook Street
Cainscross	❱	Car Park, Westward Rd (Daytime)
Dursley	❱	Castle Street Car Park (Daytime) May Lane Car Park (Daytime)
Kingswood	❱	Rectory Road (Parish Council)
Minchinhampton	❱	Bell Lane
Nailsworth	❱	Old Market Bus Station
Painswick	❱	Stamages Lane Car Park St Mary's Street (Town Council)
Stonehouse	❱	High Street Car Park
Stroud	❱	Bedford Street Brunel Mall MSCP, London Road (Daytime) Stratford Park, Stratford Road The Lord John, Russell Street (JDW)

Old Nelson, Stratford Road (Private)

Wotton-under-Edge ❯ Rope Walk (Daytime)

SWINDON

Covingham ❯ Dorcan Way (Mon-Sat, Daytime)

Gorse Hill ❯ Chapel Street (Mon-Sat, Daytime)

Highworth ❯ Highworth Recreation Centre (Centre hrs)
New Road (Mon-Sat, Daytime)

Lechlade ❯ Riverside Park (Mon-Sat, Daytime)

Swindon Town Centre ❯ Brunel Centre, Market Place (Mon-Sat, Daytime)
Bus Station, New Bridge Street (Daytime)
Oasis Leisure Centre (Centre hrs)
Town Arts Centre, Regent Circus (Centre hrs)
Town Gardens, Westlecot Street (Park hrs)
Victoria Road, Old Town (Mon-Sat, Daytime)
The Brunel Centre, 1st Floor (Private)
Debenhams Store, The Parade (Debenhams)
House of Fraser Store, Brunel Centre (Private)
Sainsbury's Store, Bridgemead (Sainsbury)
Swindon Station, Platform 1 (Gt Western)
Bell Hotel, Club Bar (Private)
Dockle Farmhouse, Bridge End Rd (JDW)
Groves Company Inn, Fleet Street (JDW)
The Savoy, Regent Street (JDW)
Sir Daniel Arms, Fleet Street (JDW)
Walkabout, Fleet Street (Private)
Yates's Bar, Bridge Street (Yates)
Gala Bingo, Greenbridge Retail Park (Gala)

South Swindon ❯ Barbury Castle Park (Park hrs)
Coate Water Country Park (Park hrs)

West Swindon ❯ Link Centre (2) (Centre hrs)
Lydiard Park, Visitor Centre (Park hrs)
West Swindon Shopping Centre
(Mon-Sat, Daytime)

Wroughton ❯ Wharf Road (unsuitable for wheelchair users)

TAUNTON DEANE

Bishops Lydeard ❯ Mount Street (8.00-20.00)
Bishops Lydeard Station (W Somerset Rly)

Taunton ❯ Canon Street Car Park (Daytime)
Castle Green (M only)
Castle Walk (F only) (Mon-Sat Daytime)
French Weir Recreation Area (Daytime)
High Street MSCP (Daytime)
Paul Street
Station Road, Flook House (Daytime)
Taunton Bus Station (Daytime)
Victoria Park (Daytime)
Vivary Park (Park hrs)
Wilton Lands, nr. Golf Club (Daytime)
Debenhams Store, North St (Debenhams)
Sainsbury's Store, Heron Gate (Sainsbury)
Taunton Station, Platforms 2 & 5 (Gt Western)
Coal Orchard, Bridge Street (JDW)
Perkin Warbeck, East Street (JDW)
Que Pasa, High Street (Marstons)
Yates's Bar, High Street (Yates)

Wellington ❯ Longforth Road (Daytime)
North Street Car Park (Daytime)
Rockwell Green, Oaken Ground
Wellington Park (Park hrs)

Wiveliscombe ❯ North Street

TEWKESBURY

Alderton ❯ Village Hall (Hall hrs) (Private)

Churchdown ❯ Parish Council Offices, Parton Road
(Parish Council)

Tewkesbury ❯ Bishop Walk, High Street (Town Council)
Tewkesbury Abbey Caravan Club Site
(Caravan Club)

Twigworth ❯ Twigworth, Tewkesbury Road (Private)

Winchcombe ❯ Back Lane Car Park (Parish Council)

WEST DORSET

Abbotsbury ❯ Back Street
Beach (Private)

Beaminster ❯ Fleet Street

Bridport ❯ East Street Car Park
Town Hall
West Street Car Park
Eype Picnic Area (SW Highways)
The Greyhound, East Street (JDW)

Buckland Newton ❯ Village Hall (Parish Council)

Burton Bradstock ❯ Village
Hive Beach (National Trust)

Cerne Abbas ❯ Long Street

Charmouth ❯ Foreshore
Village Car Park

Chideock ❯ Seatown

Dorchester ❯ Charles Street Car Park
Maumbury Road, Car Park
Top o' Town Car Park

West Country

Trinity Street Car Park
Tudor Arcade
Kingston Pond, A35 (SW Highways)
Antelope Walk (Private)
Royal Oak, High West Street (JDW)
Crossways Caravan Club Site (Caravan Club)

Lyme Regis   ❯

Broad Street
Charmouth Road (Summer)
Holmbush
Monmouth Beach
Marine Parade (Summer) (Town Council)
Woodmead Car Park (Town Council)

Sherborne   ❯

Culverhayes Car Park
Digby Road
Old Market Yard Car Park

West Bay   ❯

East Beach (Summer)
Fisherman's Green
Groves Garden Centre (Private)

West Bexington   ❯

Beach Car Park

WEST SOMERSET

Blue Anchor   ❯

Seafront, Central

Dulverton   ❯

Lion Stables Car Park
Exmoor House Caravan Club Site (Caravan Club)

Dunster   ❯

Dunster Steep Car Park

Exebridge   ❯

Lakeside Caravan Club Site (Caravan Club)

Kilve   ❯

Kilve Beach Car Park

Minehead   ❯

Blenheim Gardens
Summerland Car Park
Warren Road, Arcade
Warren Road, opp. Butlins
Minehead Station (W Somerset Rly)
Duke of Wellington, Wellington Square (JDW)
Minehead Caravan Club Site (Caravan Club)

Porlock   ❯

Central Car Park

Doverhay Car Park

Tarr Steps 〉 Tarr Steps Car Park (Exmoor NP)

Watchet 〉 Harbour Road
Market Street Car Park

Wheddon Cross 〉 Rest & Be Thankful Car Park (Parish Council)

Williton 〉 Car Park, Killick Way

WEYMOUTH & PORTLAND

Portland 〉 Easton Gardens
Ferrybridge Car Park
Portland Bill Car Park

Weymouth 〉 Brunswick Terrace, Greenhill
Cove Street, Hope Square
Littlemoor Shopping Centre
Lodmoor Car Park, Preston Road
Nothe Gardens, Barrack Road
Overcomber Corner, Preston
Southill Shopping Centre, Radipole Lane
Swannery Car Park, Radipole Park Drive
Tourist Information Centre, The Esplanade
Lower St Albans Street MSCP (Private)
Debenhams Store, New Bond St (Debenhams)
Jubilee Business Park Café (Private)
Que Pasa, St Thomas St (Marstons)
The Swan, St Thomas Street (JDW)
William Henry, Frederick Place (JDW)
Yates's Bar, St Thomas Street (Yates)
Gala Bingo, Crescent Street (Gala)

WILTSHIRE

Amesbury 〉 Central Car Park

Bradford-on-Avon 〉 St Margaret's Car Park
Station Car Park
Barton Farm Country Club (Private)

Calne 〉 The Pippin

West Country

Castle Combe	❯	The Street
Chippenham	❯	Bath Road Car Park
		Borough Parade
		Monkton Park
		Sainsbury's Store, Bath Road (Sainsbury)
		Bridge House, Borough Parade (JDW)
Corsham	❯	Newlands Road (M&F)
Cricklade	❯	off High Street
Devizes	❯	The Green
		West Central Car Park
		Silk Mercer, St Johns Street (JDW)
Downton	❯	The Borough
Kington Langley	❯	A429 Picnic Site (Wilts CC)
Lacock	❯	Red Lion Car Park (National Trust)
Leigh Delamere M4	❯	Leigh Delamere Services E, J17/18 M4 (Moto)
		Leigh Delamere Services W, J17/18 M4 (Moto)
Marlborough	❯	George Lane
Melksham	❯	Bath Road Car Park
		Church Street Car Park
		Town Square
Mere	❯	Salisbury Street Car Park
Salisbury	❯	Bemerton Recreation Ground
		Central Car Park
		Churchill Gardenst
		Coach Station
		Culver Street
		Guildhall (Guildhall hrs)
		Hudsons Field Campsite (April-October)
		Lush House, Crane Street
		Victoria Park
		Salisbury Cathedral, off Cloisters (Cathedral)
		Old George Mall Shopping Precinct (Private)
		Debenhams Store, Market Place (Debenhams)
		Salisbury Station, Platforms 2 & 4 (SW Trains)
		King's Head, Bridge Street (JDW)
		Gala Bingo, Endless Street (Private)

Steeple Langford	❯	Hillside Caravan Club Site (Caravan Club) A36 Picnic Lay-by
Tisbury	❯	Nadder Close
Trowbridge	❯	Trowbridge Park Albany Palace, Park Road (JDW) Sir Isaac Pitman, Market Place (JDW)
Warminster	❯	Central Car Park Warminster Park Longleat Caravan Club Site (Caravan Club)
Westbury	❯	High Street Car Park Warminster Road Car Park Westbury Station, Platform 1 (Gt Western)
Wilton	❯	Greyhound Lane
Wootton Bassett	❯	Boroughfields Car Park

DEVON & CORNWALL

CORNWALL

Bodmin	❯	Lanivet Car Park Dennison Road (Town Council) Fair Park (Town Council) Priory Park (Town Council) Bodmin Parkway Station (Gt Western) Chapel an Gansblydhen, Fore Street (JDW)
Boscastle	❯	Cobweb Car Park
Bude	❯	Crackington Haven The Crescent Car Park Crooklets Beach Car Park Ploughill Summerleaze Beach Summerleaze Car Park Widemouth Bay Duckpool, Car Park (National Trust)
Callington	❯	New Road
Calstock	❯	The Quay
Camborne	❯	Camborne Park Gurneys Lane Rosewarne Car Park
Camelford	❯	Enfield Park
Coverack	❯	Car Park (M&F)
Delabole	❯	High Street
Downderry	❯	Main Road
Falmouth	❯	Packet Station, The Moor (JDW)
Gunnislake	❯	by Car Park (M&F) (Daytime)
Gunwalloe	❯	Church Cove (Easter-Sept)
Gwithian	❯	Godrevy (National Trust)

Hayle	❯	Foundry Square Godrevy Park Caravan Club Site (Caravan Club)
Helford	❯	Car Park
Helston	❯	Coinagehall Street Trengrouse Way
Kilkhampton	❯	Market Square Car Park
Kingsand	❯	behind Halfway House (F only)
Kynance Cove	❯	Car Park (Easter-Sept) (Nat. Trust)
Lanner	❯	Playing Field
Launceston	❯	Cattle Market Walk House Car Park
Lelant Saltings	❯	Park & Ride (Summer)
Liskeard	❯	Sungirt Car Park Westbourne Car Park Liskeard Station (Gt Western)
Lizard	❯	The Green, Car Park
Looe	❯	Guildhall Hannafore Millpool Seafront Looe Caravan Club Site (Caravan Club)
Marazion	❯	Station Car Park
Menheniot	❯	East Road (Parish Council)
Minions	❯	-
Mullion	❯	Cove (Easter-Sept) Village Car Park
Newquay	❯	Newquay Station (Gt Western) Sailors Arms, Fore Street (Private) Towan Blystra, Cliff Road (JDW)

Devon & Cornwall

Walkabout, The Crescent (Private)

Padstow ❯ Council Offices Car Park
Link Road Car Park
South Quay

Padstow Coast ❯ Constantine Beach Car Park
Corys Shelter (F only)
Harlyn Beach
Porthcothan Beach
Trevone Beach
Treyarnon Beach

Pelynt ❯ Village Hall (Parish Council)

Pendeen ❯ Boscaswell (Daytime)

Penzance ❯ Alexandra Gardens (Daytime)
Jennings Street (Daytime)
Penalverne, nr. St Johns Hall (Daytime)
Tourist Information Centre (Daytime)
Wherrytown, Promenade (Daytime)
Wharfside Shopping Centre (Private)
Penzance Station (Gt Western)
Tremenheere, Market Place (JDW)

Poldhu ❯ Beach (Easter-Sept)

Polperro ❯ Fishna Bridge

Polruan ❯ St Saviours

Polzeath ❯ opp. The Beach
Daymer Beach
New Polzeath Car Park

Port Isaac ❯ Clifftop Car Park
Fish Cellars, Roscarrick Hill

Porthallow ❯ Porthallow Beach

Porthcurno ❯ Car Park

Porthleven ❯ Shute Lane

Portreath ❯ Beach Road

Devon & Cornwall

Portscatho	❯	Merrose Farm Caravan Club Site (Caravan Club)
Poughill	❯	-
Praa Sands	❯	Car Park
Praze-an-Beeble	❯	The Square
Redruth	❯	Fairfield (Events only) New Cut Car Park Redruth Station, Platform 2 (Gt Western)
Rejerrah	❯	Monkey Tree Holiday Park (Private)
Rose	❯	Treamble Valley Caravan Club Site (Caravan Club)
St Austell	❯	St Austell Station, Platform 1 (Gt Western) Rann Wartha, Biddicks Court (JDW)
St Ives	❯	Porthmeor Car Park (Daytime) Sloop Car Park (May-Sept, Daytime) Station Car Park (Daytime) Trenwith Car/Coach Park (Daytime) West Pier (Daytime)
St Just	❯	Lafrowda Close Car Park
St Keverne	❯	The Square
St Merryn	❯	Harlyn Road
St Teath	❯	Car Park, opp White Hart Inn
Saltash	❯	Bellevue Car Park Longstone Park (M&F) (Daytime)
Sennen	❯	Sennen Cove Car Park (Summer)
Torpoint	❯	Antony Road Thanckes Park Ferry Queuing Lanes (Torpoint Ferry)
Tintagel	❯	Bossinney The Castle

		Fore Street, Trevenna Square
		Trerammett
		Visitor Centre
		Trewethett Farm Caravan Club Site (Caravan Club)
Trebarwith	❯	Trebarwith Strand
Truro	❯	Truro Station, Platform 2 (Gt Western)
		Barley Sheaf, Old Bridge Street (Private)
		Try Dower, Lemon Quay (JDW)
Wadebridge	❯	Egloshayle Road
		Goldsworthy Way Car Park
		The Platt

EAST DEVON

Axminster	❯	West Street Car Park
Beer	❯	Jubilee Gardens
Branscombe	❯	Beach Car Park
		Village Hall Car Park
Broadclyst	❯	Victory Hall Car Park
Budleigh Salterton	❯	Brook Road Car Park (F only)
		East End, Lime Kiln Seafront
Colyton	❯	Dolphin Street Car Park
Exmouth	❯	Bus/Rail Station (M&F)
		Elizabeth Hall Grounds
		Foxholes Car Park
		Imperial Grounds, opp Car Park
		Lifeboat
		Maer Park
		Manor Gardens, by Town Hall
		Phear Park
		Templetown
		Powder Monkey, The Parade (JDW)
Honiton	❯	King Street Car Park
		Lace Walk Car Park

Lympstone ❯ Underhill Car Park

Newton Poppleford ❯ School Lane Car Park

Otterton ❯ The Square

Ottery St Mary ❯ Flexton, Town Centre
Hind Street Car Park

Seaton ❯ Chine, west of West Walk Esplanade
Harbour Road Car Park
Marsh Road, by Town Hall
West Walk

Sidmouth ❯ Connaught Gardens
Market Place
Port Royal
Triangle
Long Park, Woolbrook
Putts Corner Caravan Club Site (Caravan Club

EXETER

Exeter City Centre ❯ Blackboy Road
King William Street
Musgrave Row
Paris Street
The Quay
Princesshay Exeter, Catherine St (Private)
Exeter St Davids Station (Gt Western)
Butlers, Mary Arches Street (Private)
George's Meeting House, South St (JDW)
The Imperial, New North Road (JDW)
Nandos, 32 Princess Hay (Nandos)
Pitcher & Piano, Queen Street (Private)
Walkabout, Fore Street (Private)

Exeter St Thomas ❯ Cowick Barton Playing Fields
Cowick Street Railway Arch
Okehampton Street
St Thomas Pleasure Ground
Sawyers Arms, Cowick Street (JDW)

Exwick ❯ Ennerdale Way

Heavitree ❯ Fore Street
Heavitree Park

Matford ❯ Park & Ride

Polsloe ❯ Hamlin Lane
Railwayman, Pinhoe Road (Private)

Topsham ❯ Fore Street
Topsham Quay

Whipton ❯ Pinhoe Road, nr. shops

ISLES OF SCILLY

St Mary's ❯ Old Weslyan Chapel, Garrison Lane

MID DEVON

Bampton ❯ Luke Street

Chawleigh ❯ Village Hall (Daytime)

Crediton ❯ Market Street
Newcombes Meadow
General Sir Redvers Buller, High St (JDW)

Cullompton ❯ Station Road

Down St Mary ❯ Morchard Road, A377 Picnic Area

Hemyock ❯ Culmbridge Road, by Parish Hall

Sampford Peverell ❯ Recreation Ground
Tiverton Parkway Station (Gt Western)

Tiverton ❯ Lowman Green
Market Car Park
Peoples Park
Phoenix Lane
Westexe South
Canal Basin Car Park (Devon CC)
White Ball Inn, Bridge Street (JDW)

NORTH DEVON

Blackmoor Gate ❯ Car Park, A399 (Exmoor NP)

Barnstaple ❯ Old Cattlemarket Car Park [March 09]
Pannier Market
Pilton Park
Rock Park
North Devon Library & Record Office (Devon CC)
Green Lanes Shopping Centre (Private)
Sainsbury's Store, Gratton Way (Sainsbury)
Panniers, Boutport Street (JDW)
Water Gate, The Strand (JDW)

Braunton ❯ Caen Street Car Park

Combe Martin ❯ Kiln Car Park

Croyde ❯ Croyde Beach
Down End Car Park

Ilfracombe ❯ Bicclescombe Park
The Cove
The Pier
Town Council Offices
Wilder Road Car Park

Instow ❯ Marine Drive Car Park
Sandy Lane

Devon & Cornwall

Mortehoe	❷	Damage Barton Caravan Club Site (Caravan Club)
Saunton	❷	Beach Toilets
South Molton	❷	Pannier Market (Daytime)
Woolacombe	❷	Willingcott Caravan Club Site (Caravan Club)

PLYMOUTH

| City Centre | ❷ | Armada Way, off Ladies (Daytime)
Civic Centre, Royal Parade (Office hrs)
Barbican, Quay (Daytime)
Bretonside Bus Station, off Gents (Daytime)
Hoe Promenade (Daytime)
Midland House, Notte Street (Office hrs)
Phoenix Wharf (Daytime)
Plymouth Market, Cornwall Street (Market hrs)
Tinside Lido, The Barbican (Lido hrs)
Tavistock Road, by Library (Daytime)
West Hoe (Daytime)
Debenhams Store, Royal Parade (Debenhams)
House of Fraser Store, Royal Parade (HoF)
Drake Circus Shopping Centre (Private) (CP)
Plymouth Station, Platform 4 (Gt Western)
Discovery Café, Eastlake Street (Private)
Gog & Magog, Southside Street (JDW) |

Ha! Ha! Bar, Princess Street (Private)
Hogshead, Royal Parade (Private)
Nandos, Barbican Leisure Park (Nandos)
The Union Rooms, Union Street (JDW)
Varsity, Derry's Cross (Barracuda)
Walkabout, Derry's Cross (Private)
Watering Hole, Quay Road, Barbican (Private)
Yates's Bar, Royal Parade (Yates)
Gala Bingo, Derrys Cross (Gala)
Vue Cinema, Barbican Leisure Park (Private)

Crown Hill ❯ KFC, Crown Hill Retail Park (KFC)
Tamar, Moorshead Road (Private)

Devonport ❯ Ferry Approach Lanes (Torpoint Ferry)

Estover ❯ Asda Store, Estover Shopping Centre (Asda)

Lipson ❯ Freedom Park (Café hrs)

Marsh Mills ❯ Coypool Park & Ride (Daytime)

Mawnamead ❯ Hartley Park

Milehouse ❯ Britannia Inn, Wolseley Street (JDW)

Mount Wise ❯ Mutton Cove (May-September)

Mutley ❯ Mutley Plain
The Mannamead, Mutley Plain (JDW)

Plympton ❯ The Ridgeway, Plymco Car Park (Daytime)

Plymstock ❯ Dean Hill (Daytime)

St Budeaux ❯ Wolseley Road

Stoke ❯ Masterman Road (Daytime)

Stonehouse ❯ Cremyll Street (Daytime)
Devil's Point (Daytime)

Tamar Bridge ❯ Bridge Car Park, A38 (Tamar Bridge)

Turnchapel ❯ Lawrence Road, Mountbatten Car Park
(Daytime)

| West Hooe | ❯ | Jennycliff Car Park (Daytime) |

SOUTH HAMS

Modbury	❯	Broad Park Caravan Club Site (Caravan Club)
Stoke Gabriel	❯	Ramslade Caravan Club Site (Caravan Club)
Stokenham	❯	Start Bay Caravan Club Site (Caravan Club)
Totnes	❯	Totnes Station (Gt Western)

TEIGNBRIDGE

Abbotskerwell	❯	Bottom of Church Path
Ashburton	❯	Kingsbridge Lane Car Park
Bovey Tracey	❯	Station Road
Buckfastleigh	❯	Coach Park
Dawlish	❯	Barton Hill
		Boat Cove (Daytime)
		The Lawn, by Tourist Information Centre
		Sandy Lane (Daytime)
		Dawlish Station, Platform 2 (Gt Western)

Teignbridge

DISTRICT COUNCIL
South Devon

For more information on toilet facilities and access, why not telephone before you travel?

Please telephone for all enquiries:

01626 215 838

Dawlish Warren ❯ Beach Road Car Park
Sea Front

Newton Abbot ❯ Cricketfield Car Park
Decoy Country Park, Car Park
Market Walk
Newfoundland Way
Newton Abbot Station, Platform 3 (Gt Western)
Richard Hopkins, Queen Street (JDW)

Shaldon ❯ The Strand

Starcross ❯ The Strand (Summer, Daytime)

Teignmouth ❯ Brunswick Street
Lower Brook Street (Daytime)
Teignmouth Station, Platform 1 (Gt Western)

Widecombe ❯ The Green Car Park

TORBAY

Brixham ❯ Bank Lane (Daytime)
Berry Head
Brixham Harbour (Daytime)
Shoalstone Beach (April-October, Daytime)
The Vigilance, Bolton Street (JDW)
Hillhead Holiday Park (Caravan Club)

Paignton ❯ Broadsands Beach (Daytime)
Festival Apollo (April-October, Daytime)
Goodrington Central (Daytime)
Palace Avenue (8.00-20.00)
Paignton Central (Daytime)
Parkside/Victoria Square (Daytime)
Preston North, Marine Drive (Daytime)
Quaywest Central (Private)
The Isaac Merritt", Torquay Road (JDW)
Noahs ArK, Totnes Road (Private)
Gala Bingo, Temperance Street (Gala)

Torquay ❯ Abbey Meadows (April-October, 9.00-19.00)
Beacon Quay (Daytime)
Corbyn Head (April-October, 9.00-19.00)
Factory Row, off Union Street (Daytime)
Lymington Road, Coach Station (Daytime)

Meadfoot Beach (April-October, 9.00-19.00)
Oddicombe Beach (April-October, 9.00-19.00)
Old Town Hall, Union Street (Daytime)
St Marychurch Town Hall, Manor Road
(7.00-21.00)
Seafront Complex (Daytime)
Vaughan Parade (Daytime)
Cockington Car Park (Private)
Fleet Walk Shopping Centre (Private)
Torquay Station, Platform 1 (Gt Western)
Babbacombe Inn, Babbacombe Downs (Private)
Bar Med, Fleetwalk Centre (Private)
Hog's Head, Union Street (Private)
London Inn, The Strand (JDW)
Manor Inn, Market Street (Private)
Shiraz, Vaughan Parade (Private)
Yates's Bar, Swan Street (Yates)
Torquay Bowl, Torwood Street (AMF)

TORRIDGE

Appledore ⊙ Churchfields Car Park (Daytime)

Bideford ⊙ Bideford Quay
Victoria Park (8.00-18.00)

Bradworthy ⊙ The Square

Halwill Junction ⊙ Playing Field

Torrington ⊙ The Commons (Daytime)
South Street (Daytime)

Westward Ho ⊙ Main Putting Green (Daytime)
Slipway Car Park (Daytime)

Winkleigh ⊙ Castle Street

WEST DEVON

Chagford ⊙ Community Centre Car Park

Meldon ⊙ Meldon Quarry Station (Dartmoor Rlwy)

Okehampton ⊙ Market Street, by Taxi Rank

Fairplace, George Street
Okehampton Station (Dartmoor Rlwy)

Princetown ❯ Information Centre Car Park

Tavistock ❯ Bedford Car Park
Guildhall Car Park
Tavistock Wharf

Yelverton ❯ Roundabout

Bringing down the barriers

The National Union of Teachers has led the way in campaigning against the inequalities and discrimination faced by disabled children and teachers.

The NUT is actively campaigning:

- to protect services that support pupils with special education needs;
- for each local authority to be required to provide a full range of special education provision;
- for local authorities to improve disability access to all schools;
- to protect the rights of all children to education; and
- for equal opportunities for disabled teachers in recruitment, retention and career development.

**For further information on the NUT's policies write to the
Disability Equality Officer, Education and Equal Opportunities,
National Union of Teachers, Hamilton House,
Mabledon Place, London WC1H 9BD.**

Membership Joining Hotline 0845 300 1669

6256a/01/09

EASTERN ENGLAND

BABERGH

Chelmondiston	❯	Pin Mill
East Bergholt	❯	Flatford Visitor Centre Red Lion Car Park
Lavenham	❯	Cock Inn Car Park Prentice Street Car Park
Long Melford	❯	Cordell Road The Green
Rodbridge	❯	Rodbridge Picnic Site (Suffolk CC)
Sudbury	❯	Grover & Allen, North Street (JDW)

BASILDON

Basildon	❯	Basildon Library (Library hrs) (Essex CC) Eastgate Business Centre (3) (Private) Eastgate Shopping Centre (3) (Private) Market Square (Private) Basildon Station, Booking Hall (C2C) Moon on the Square, Market Square (JDW) Nandos, Eastgate (Nandos) Nandos, Festival Leisure Park (Nandos) Towngate, Westgate Park (Private) Yates's Bar, Swan Street (Yates) Nethermayne Campus (Thurrock & Basildon College)
Billericay	❯	Blue Boar, High Street (JDW) Red Lion, High Street (Private)
Laindon	❯	Shopping Centre (M&F) (Mon-Sat, daytime) Laindon Station, Platform 3 (C2C)
Pitsea	❯	Pitsea Station, Booking Hall (C2C)
Wickford	❯	Woodford Road (Mon-Sat, 8.00-16.30) Downtowner Youth Centre (Centre hrs) (Essex CC)

The Willows Shopping Centre (Private)
Wickford Station (NX East Anglia)
Royal British Legion Club (RBL)

BEDFORD

Bedford Town Centre ❯❯ Allhallows Bus Station (M&F) (7.00-18.30)
Bedford Park East
Corn Exchange (when open)
Riverside Square (8.00-18.00)
St Pauls Square
Debenhams Store, High Street (Debenhams)
Bedford Station, Platform 1 (Capital Connect)
Bankers Draft, High Street (JDW)
Nandos, High Street (Nandos)
Pilgrims Progress, Midland Road (JDW)
Que Pasa, St Pauls Square (Marstons)

East Bedford ❯❯ Priory Country Park (8.00-18.00)
Russell Park (8.00-17.00, later in Summer)

Kempston ❯❯ Addison Howard Park (Park hrs)

BRAINTREE

Braintree ❯❯ Victoria St. Bus Park (8.00-17.00)
Braintree Library, Fairfield Rd (Library hrs)
(Essex CC)
Braintree Station, Ticket Office (NX East Anglia)
Baileys Café Bar, High Street (Private)
Barracuda, High Street (Barracuda)
Picture Palace, Fairfield Road (JDW)

Castle Hedingham ❯❯ Memorial Lane (8.00-17.00)

Earls Colne ❯❯ Queens Road Car Park (8.00-17.00)

Finchingfield ❯❯ Stephen Marshall Avenue (8.00-17.00)

Halstea ❯❯ Kings Road (8.00-17.00)

Witham ❯❯ Lockrams Lane (8.00-17.00)
Witham Library (Library hrs) (Essex CC)
Witham Station (NX East Anglia)
Battesford Court, Newland Street (JDW)

BRECKLAND

Attleborough ➤ Queens Square, Car Park (Daytime)
(Town Council)

Dereham ➤ Barwells Court, Market Place (Town Council)
Cowper Road, Car Park (Daytime)
(Town Council)

Roudham Heath ➤ Rest Area (Highway Authority)

Swaffham ➤ The Shambles, Market Place (Town Council)

Thetford ➤ Bridge Street Car Park (Town Council)
Cage Lane (Town Council)
Castle Park, Castle Street (Town Council)

Watton ➤ St Giles Car Park (Daytime) (Town Council)

BRENTWOOD

Brentwood ➤ Brentwood Station
High Street (7.30-19.30)
Nandos, High Street (Nandos)

Ingatestone ➤ Market Place (Mon-Sat, 8.00-18.00)

Shenfield ➤ Shenfield Station, Platform 3 (NX East Anglia)

West Horndon ➤ West Horndon Station, Ticket Hall (C2C)

BROADLAND

Acle ➤ The Street, by Kings Head

Ranworth ➤ The Staithe, opp. The Maltsters (April-October)

Salhouse ➤ Salhouse Broad Car Park (M&F) (April-Oct)

Thorpe St Andrew ➤ River Green, Yarmouth Road (April-Oct)

BROXBOURNE

Broxbourne ➤ Deaconsfield, High Road

Old Mill Meadows Car Park (Lee Valley RPA)

Cheshunt ❯ Grundy Park, Turners Hill (Daytime)
Pindar Car Park (Lee Valley RPA)
King James, Turners Hill (JDW)

Hoddesdon ❯ Tower Centre, Amwell Street (Daytime)

Waltham Cross ❯ Supermarket Car Park, High Street (M&F) (Daytime)
Highbridge Car Park (Lee Valley RPA)
The Moon & Cross, High Street (JDW)

CAMBRIDGE

Cambridge ❯ Arbury Court, nr. shops (8.00-18.00)
Cherry Hinton Hall (Daytime)
Chesterton Recreation Ground (Daytime)
Chesterton Road, by Mitcham's Corner (Daytime)
Coleridge Recreation Ground (April-Oct, Daytime)
Drummer Street Bus Station (8.00-20.00)
Guildhall, Market Square (Office hrs)
Jesus Green (Daytime)
Kings Hedges Recreation Ground (April-Oct, Daytime)
Lammas Land, nr Paddling Pool (Daytime)
Lion Yard Shopping Centre (8.00-20.00)
Nightingale Recreation Ground (Daytime)
Park Street MSCP (8.00-20.00)
Quayside, off Bridge Street (8.00-20.00)
Silver Street, by bridge (8.00-20.00)
Grafton Centre, by Shopmobility (Private)
Grafton Centre, Eden Court (Private)
Debenhams Store, Grafton Centre (Debenhams)
Cambridge Station, Platform 1 (NX East Anglia)
McDonalds, Rose Crescent (McDonalds)
Nandos, Cambridge Leisure Park (Nandos)
Nandos, St Andrews Street (Nandos)
Rat & Parrot, Downing Street (Private)
The Regal, St Andrew's Street (JDW)
Helmore Building, East Road (Anglia Ruskin University)
Corn Exchange (2) (Centre hrs)
Mumford Theatre (Theatre hrs) (Private)
Cherry Hinton Caravan Club Site (Caravan Club)

CASTLE POINT

Benfleet ❯ Richmond Hall
Tarpot Car Park, Rushbottom Lane
Benfleet Station, Platform 1 (C2C)

Canvey Island ❯ Knightswick Shopping Centre
Labworth, Western Esplanade
Lubbins Car Park, Eastern Esplanade

Hadleigh ❯ Rectory Road, Car park

CHELMSFORD

Boreham ❯ Grange, Main Road (Private)

Chelmsford ❯ Admirals Park, near footbridge (Daytime)
Central Park, by Bowling Pavilion (Park hrs)
Dovedale Sports Centre (Centre hrs)
Hylands Park, by parking area (Daytime)
Lionmead Park, Sandford Road (Daytime)
Melbourne Park, parking area (Daytime)
Moulesham Street/Hamlet Road
Oaklands Park (Park hrs)
Shopmobility, Market Road (Daytime)
Waterloo Lane, by Pool
The Meadows Shopping Centre (Private)
Sainsbury's Store, Springfield (Sainsbury)
Chelmsford Station (NX East Anglia)
Ladbrokes, Clematis Tye (Ladbrokes)
Baroosh Restaurant, Moulsham Rd (Private)
The Fleece, Duke Street (Private)
Ivory Peg, New London Road (JDW)
Que Pasa, Springfield Rd (Marstons)
Thomas Mildmay, Springfield Road (JDW)
Ashby House, Bishop Hall Road (Anglia Ruskin University)
Odeon Cinema, Kings Head Walk (Odeon)
Tenpin, Widford Industrial Estate (Private)

Danbury ❯ Main Road, by Cricket Ground

Galleywood ❯ Watchouse Road (Daytime)

Writtle ❯ The Green (Daytime)
Horse & Groom (Private)

Woodham Ferrers	❯	by Railway Station (Daytime)

by Railway Station (Daytime)
South Woodham Ferrers Leisure Centre
(Centre hrs)
Starz Youth Centre (Centre hrs) (Essex CC)
William de Ferrers Adult Educ. Centre
(Essex CC)

COLCHESTER

Colchester ❯ Castle Park, by Boating Lake
Castle Park, behind Hollytrees
Cemetery, Mersea Road
High Woods Country Park
Queen Street Bus Station
St John's Street MSCP
St Mary's MSCP, Balkerne Hill
Colchester Library (Library hrs) (Essex CC)
Sir Isaac's Walk (Private)
Osborne Street MSCP (Private)
Colchester Station (NX East Anglia)
Nandos, Head Street (Nandos)
The Playhouse, St John Street (JDW)
Yates's Bar, Head Street (Yates)
Gala Bingo, Osborne Street (Gala)

Dedham ❯ Driftway

Great Horkesley ❯ Yew Tree (Private)

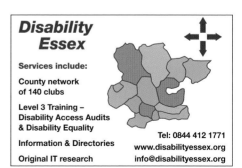

Tiptree	❯	Church Road
West Mersea	❯	Coast Road Car Park High Street Victoria Esplanade (M&F)
Wivenhoe	❯	High Street Car Park Sports Centre, Wivenhoe Park (University)

DACORUM

Apsley	❯	Durrants Hill Road
Berkhamstead	❯	Water Lane Car Park, off High Street The Crown, High Street (JDW) Old Mill, London Road (Private)
Hemel Hempstead	❯	Gadebridge Park Market Square Bus Station Woodwells Cemetery (Cemetery hrs) Marlowes Shopping Centre (Private) Nash Mills Boat Base (Summer) (Private) The Full House, The Marlowes (JDW)
Kings Langley	❯	High Street Kings Langley Station (London Midland)
Ringshall	❯	Ashridge Estate, by Visitor Centre (National Trust
Tring	❯	Market Place Car Park, High Street

EAST CAMBRIDGESHIRE

Ely	❯	Barton Road Car Park (8.00-18.00) Cloisters Shopping Centre (8.00-18.00) Newnham Street Car Park Sacrist Gate, by Cathedral (8.00-18.00) Ship Lane Car Park, Riverside Ely Station, Platform 1 (NX East Anglia)
Littleport	❯	Main Street Car Park (8.00-17.00)
Soham	❯	Fountain Lane Car Park (7.30-19.30)
Wicken Fen	❯	Lode Lane car park, near Nature Reserve Wren Building (National Trust)

EAST HERTFORDSHIRE

Bishops Stortford ❯ Castle Gardens
Riverside Walk
Bishops Stortford Station, Platform 1
(NX East Anglia)

Buntingford ❯ Bowling Green Lane

Hertford ❯ Bircherley Green, nr. Bus Station
Hartham Common
Hertford East Station (NX East Anglia)
Six Templars, The Wash (JDW)

Sawbridgeworth ❯ Bell Street Car Park

Spellbrook ❯ Three Horseshoes, Spellbrook Lane (Private)

Ware ❯ Amwell End/Broadmeads
Priory Street (Town Council)

EPPING FOREST

Buckhurst Hill ❯ Lower Queens Road

Epping ❯ Bakers Lane Car Park

High Beech ❯ by Information Centre (City of London)

Hoddesdon ❯ Dobbs Weir Car Park (Lee Valley RPA)

Loughton ❯ The Broadway
Brook Path, High Road
Traps Hill Car Park
The Last Post, High Road (JDW)

Ongar ❯ High Street

Waltham Abbey ❯ Quaker Lane Car Park
Fishers Green Car Park (Lee Valley RPA)
High Bridge Street (Town Council)
Bakers Arms, Stewardstone Road (Private)

FENLAND

Chatteris	❯	Furrowfields Station Street
March	❯	Broad Street City Road Car Park
Whittlesey	❯	Eastgate Car Park Station Road
Wisbech	❯	Church Terrace Car Park Exchange Square Wisbech Park Horsefair Shopping Centre (Private) Wheatsheaf Inn, Church Terrace (JDW)

FOREST HEATH

Brandon	❯	Brandon Country Park (Suffolk CC)
Lakenheath	❯	Wings Road (07.00-19.00)
Mildenhall	❯	Recreation Way
Newmarket	❯	Memorial Gardens, High Street Golden Lion, High Street (JDW)

GREAT YARMOUTH

Caister	❯	Beach Road Car Park (Easter-October) High Street Second Avenue (Easter-October) Yarmouth Stadium (Stadium hrs) (Private) Grasmere Caravan Park (Private)
Gorleston	❯	Brush Quay High Street, opp. Feathers Pier Head, by Ocean Rooms Ravine Bridge, Marine Parade
Great Yarmouth	❯	Alpha Road/Southtown Road Caister Road/Beaconsfield Road The Conge, off Market Place The Jetty, Seafront

Marina Beach (7.00-21.00) (Easter-Oct)
Market Gates Precinct (M&F) (7.00-21.00)
North Beach, Seafront
South Beach (Easter-October)
The Tower, Marine Parade
Great Yarmouth Station (NX East Anglia)
The Troll Cart, Regent Road (JDW)
Great Yarmouth Racecourse Caravan Site
(Caravan Club)
Vauxhall Holiday Park (2) (Private)

Hemsby ❯ Beach Road

Martham ❯ Village Green

Winterton ❯ Beach Car Park

HARLOW

Harlow ❯ Bus Station, Terminus Street
Bush Fair
London Road, Old Harlow
Shopmobility Car Park
Staple Tye, by Shopping Precinct (M&F)
(Daytime)
The Stow, by Car Park
Town Park, Greyhound Car Park
Town Park, Pets Corner
Harlow Town Station, Ticket Hall (NX East Anglia)

FENLAND DISTRICT COUNCIL
Disabled toilet facilities within Fenland

MARCH
Broad Street & City Road car park

WHITTLESEY
Eastgate car park & Station Road

WISBECH
Church Terrace car park,
Exchange Square & Wisbech Park

CHATTERIS
Furrowfields & Station Street

For more information call 01354 654321

Nandos, The Water Gardens (Nandos)
William Aylmer, Kitson Way (JDW)
Yates's Bar, Eastgate (Yates)

HERTSMERE

Borehamwood ❯
Station Road
Hart & Spool, Shenley Road (JDW)
Gala Bingo, Boulevard Park (Gala)

Bushey ❯
King George Recreation Ground
Rudolph Road

Potters Bar ❯
Oakmere Park, High Street
Admiral Byng, Darkes Lane (JDW)

Radlett ❯
Radlett Station, Platform 4 (Capital Connect)

Shenley ❯
London Road

HUNTINGDONSHIRE

Godmanchester ❯
School Hill/Post Street

Grafham Water ❯
Mander Car Park (Anglia Water)
Grafham Water Caravan Club Site
(Caravan Club)

Huntingdon	❯	Benedict's Court, Waitrose Complex Bus Station [To be redeveloped] Hinchingbrooke Country Park Riverside Pavilion, Hartford Road Grammar School Walk Car Park (Private) Shopmobility Centre, Princess St Car Park (Shopmobility)
Ramsey	❯	New Street/Great Whyte [To be redeveloped]
St Ives	❯	Bus Station, Station Road/Cattlemarket West Street Car Park, Globe Place
St Neots	❯	Riverside Park, Car Park South Street [To be closed] Tebbuts Road, Car Park

IPSWICH

Ipswich	❯	Alexandra Park (Park hrs) Bourne Park, by Depot (Park hrs) Chantry Park, Hadleigh Road (Park hrs) Christchurch Park (3) (Park hrs) Civic Drive Holywell Park (Park hrs) Old Cattle Market Bus Station Old Foundry Road Tower Ramparts Bus Station Buttermarket Centre (2) (Private) Tower Ramparts Centre (Private) Ipswich Station (NX East Anglia) Debenhams Store, Westgate St (Debenhams) The Cricketers, Crown Street (JDW) Nandos, Cardinal Leisure Park (Nandos) Old Orleans, Cardinal Park (Private) Robert Ransome, Tower Street (JDW)

KING'S LYNN & WEST NORFOLK

Brancaster	❯	Beach Car Park, Broads Lane
Downham Market	❯	Wales Court, Bridge Street (Daytime) Downham Market Station, Platform 1 (Capital Connect)

Heacham ❯ North Beach, Jubilee Road
South Beach Road (7.00-17.00)

Hilgay ❯ Quayside (Apr-Oct)

Holme ❯ Beach Road

Hunstanton ❯ Bowling Green (7.00-17.00)
Bus Station, Westgate
Central Promenade, Seagate
Cliff Top, Light House Close
Esplanade Gardens
Seagate Road (April-October)

King's Lynn ❯ Baker Lane Car Park (7.30-18.00)
Bus Station
Kings Lynn Station, off Platform 1 (Capital Connect)
The Globe, King Street (JDW)
Lattice House, Chapel Street (JDW)
Nandos, High Street (Nandos)
Kings Lynn Campus, Front Block (W Anglia College)

Sandringham ❯ Sandringham Country Park (Private)
Sandringham Caravan Club Site (Caravan Club)

Snettisham ❯ Snettisham Beach

LUTON

Luton ❯ Bramingham Road
Bury Street, High Town
Bus Station
Church Street, by Arndale Centre
Dunstable Road, Kingsway
Farley Hill
The Hat Factory (Centre hrs)
Old Bedford Road, Wardown Park [May 2010]
Purley Centre, Purway Close
St George's Square, Bute Street
Sundon Park Road, Hill Rise
The Mall Luton, Cheapside Square (Private)
The Mall Luton, Market Hall (Private)
Debenhams Store, Arndale Centre

(Debenhams)
Luton Station, Platforms 3/4 (Capital Connect)
Luton Parkway Station (Capital Connect)
Nandos, Galaxy Centre (Nando)
White House, Bridge Street (JDW)

MALDON

Burnham-on-Crouch ❯ Doctor's Lane, The Quay (Daytime)
Riverside Park

Heybridge ❯ Bentalls Shopping Centre (Private)

Maldon ❯ Butt Lane Car Park
Promenade Coach Park
Promenade Park Sea Wall
Kings Head Centre (Private)

Southminster ❯ High Street Car Park

Tollesbury ❯ Woodrolfe Road

MID SUFFOLK

Barham ❯ Barham Picnic Site (Suffolk CC)

Bramford ❯ Picnic Site, Ship Lane (Suffolk CC)

Eye ❯ Cross Street Car Park

Needham Market ❯ The Lake
Barratts Lane (Town Council)

Stowmarket ❯ Milton Road Car Park
Recreation Ground, Finborough Road
(Town Council)
Wilkes Way (Town Council)

NORTH HERTFORDSHIRE

Ashwell ❯ Ashridge Farm Caravan Club Site (Caravan Club)

Letchworth ❯ Central Approach (Daytime) (Private)
Three Magnets, Leys Avenue (JDW)

NORTH NORFOLK

Bacton ❯ Coast Road

Blakeney ❯ The Quay

Cromer ❯ Cadogan Road
Meadow Road Car Park
Melbourne
Pier (mid-March-October)
Rocket House (Café hrs)
Runton Road (mid-March – December)
Seacroft Caravan Club Site (Caravan Club)

East Runton ❯ Water Lane (March-December)

Fakenham ❯ Bridge Street
Highfields
Queens Road
Fakenham Racecourse Caravan Club Site
(Caravan Club)

Happisburgh ❯ Cart Gap (mid-March - Sept)

Hickling ❯ Staithe

Holt ❯ Albert Street
Country Park

Horning ❯ Swan Car Park

Hoveton ❯ Station Road

Ludham ❯ Ludham Bridge
Broadlands Caravan Club Site (Caravan Club)

Mundesley ❯ Marina Road

North Walsham ❯ New Road, Car Park

Overstrand ❯ Pauls Lane Car Park (March – Dec and weekends)

Potter Heigham ❯ Bridge

Sea Palling ❯ Beach Road

Sheringham ➤ East Promenade (March-October)
High Street
Station Approach
West Promenade
Sheringham Park (National Trust)

Stalham ➤ High Street

Walcott ➤ Coast Road

Walsingham ➤ High Street

Wells-next-the-Sea ➤ Newgate Lane
Quay, Beach Road

West Runton ➤ Incleboro Field Caravan Club Site
(Caravan Club)

NORWICH

Norwich ➤ Chapelfield Gardens Park (Park hrs)
City Hall, St Peters Street (Office hrs)
Eaton Park (Park hrs)
Memorial Gardens, St Peter's Street (Mon-Sat)
St Giles MSCP, St Giles Street
St Saviours Lane (Mon-Sat)
Tombland
Waterloo Park
Wensum Park (Apr-Oct, Park hrs)
Norwich Magistrates Court (Courts Service)
Anglia Square (Private)
The Mall Norwich (3) (Private)
Co-op Store, St Stephens Street (Co-op)
Debenhams Store, Orford Place (Debenhams)
Jarrolds Store, London Street (Private)
Norwich Station (NX East Anglia)
Auberge, Castle Mall (Private)
Bell Hotel, Orford Hill (JDW)
Forget-me-Not Café, Redwell Street (Private)
Glass House, Wensum Street (JDW)
Ha! Ha! Bar, Tombland/Upper King St (Private)
Henrys, Haymarket (Private)
KFC, Dereham Road (KFC)
KFC, Prince of Wales Road (KFC)
Maid Marian, Ipswich Road (Private)
Nandos, 23 Red Lion Street (Nandos)

Nandos, 7b Riverside Leisure Park (Nandos)
Norwegian Blue, Riverside Leisure Park (Private)
Queen of Iceni, Riverside Leisure Park (JDW)
Wagon & Horses, Dereham Road (Private)
The Whiffler, Boundary Road (JDW)
Yates's Bar, Queens Street (Yates)
Cinema City, St Andrews Street (Private)
Norfolk Showground Caravan Club Site
(Caravan Club)

PETERBOROUGH

Peterborough ●

Alma Road, Millfield (Daytime)
Car Haven Car Park (Daytime)
Newark Avenue/Eastfield Road (Daytime)
Northminster MSCP (Daytime)
Orton Mere (Daytime)
St Peters Arcade, Bridge Street
Welland Road (Daytime)
Rivergate Shopping Centre (Private)
Peterborough Station, Platforms 2 & 5 (East Coast)
Mencap Business Support Centre, Hampton
(CP) (Mencap)
College Arms, The Broadway (JDW)
Drapers Arms, Cowgate (JDW)
Peterborough Bowl, Sturrock Way, Bretton (AMF)
Ferry Meadows Caravan Club Site
(Caravan Club)

ROCHFORD

Ashingdon ●

Ashingdon Recreation Fields
Victory Inn, Ashingdon Rd (Private)

Great Wakering ●

High Street

Hockley ●

Hockley Road Car Park
Hockley Woods Car Park

Hullbridge ●

Pooles Lane

Rayleigh ●

Crown Hill
Warehouse Centre (Private)
Roebuck, High Street (JDW)
Travellers Joy, Down Hall Road (Private)

Rochford ❯ Back Lane
Rochford Station (NX East Anglia)
Anne Boleyn, Southend Road (Private)

Wallasea Island ❯ Riverside Village Holiday Park (Private)

ST ALBANS

Chiswell Green ❯ Three Hammers, Watford Road (Private)

Harpenden ❯ The George, High Street (Private)

London Colney ❯ High Street (Daytime)

Redbourne ❯ High Street Car Park

St Albans ❯ Alban Arena, Foyer (Centre hrs)
Alban Arena Car Park (M&F) (Daytime)
Clarence Park, Bowling Green (Park hrs)
Clarence Park, Ornamental Park (Park hrs)
Drovers Way, Car Park
Hatfield Road Cemetery (Cemetery hrs)
Park Street
The Ridgeway, Marshalswick, by Library
Tourist & Information Centre, Town Hall (Centre hrs)
Verulamium Park, Causeway (M&F)
Verulamium Changing Rooms (M&F)
Westminster Lodge Running Track

Rochford
District Council

For more information on public facilities and access at many attractions, you can either telephone us on

01702 546 366

or visit our website at

www.rochford.gov.uk

The Maltings, off Victoria Street (Private)
Jubilee Centre, Church Street (Private)
Cross Keys, Chequer Street (JDW)
Inn on the Park, Verulamium Park (Private)
Nandos, Chequer Street (Nandos)
Waterend Barn, St Peters Street (JDW)

Sandridge ❯ High Street Car Park

Wheathampstead ❯ East Lane Car Park
The Bull, High Street (Beefeater)

ST EDMUNDSBURY

Bury St Edmunds ❯ Abbey Gardens, Angel Hill
Bus Station
Hardwick Heath, Hardwick Lane (8.30-dusk)
Nelson Road (Daytime)
Nowton Park
Ram Meadow
West Stow Country Park (Park hrs)
Bury St Edmunds Station (NX East Anglia)

Clare ❯ Clare Castle Country Park

Haverhill ❯ Jubilee Walk
Recreation Ground, Recreation Road
Council Offices (Office hrs)
Drabbet Smock, Peas Hill (JDW)

Knettishall Heath ❯ Knettishall Country Park (Suffolk CC)

SOUTH CAMBRIDGESHIRE

Linton ❯ Dog & Duck (Private)

Milton ❯ Milton Country Park

SOUTH NORFOLK

Diss ❯ Mere Mouth, behind TIC

Harleston ❯ Bullock Fair Car Park

Hingham ❯ Market Place

Loddon	❯	Church Plain, High Street
Long Stratton	❯	Swan Lane Car Park
Wymondham	❯	Market Place

SOUTHEND-ON-SEA

Chalkwell	❯	Chalkwell Esplanade, opp. Station Chalkwell Park, London Road
Leigh	❯	Belfairs Park, Eastwood Road North Bell Wharf, Old Leigh High Street Eastwood Park, Rayleigh Road Elm Road, between Rectory Rd & Broadway Sutherland Boulevard/London Road Leigh-on-Sea Station, Concourse (C2C) The Elms, London Road (JDW) Sarah Moor, Elm Road (Private)
Shoeburyness	❯	George Street, East Beach Car Park Ness Road Shoebury Common, Car Park Shoebury Park, Elm Road Shoeburyness Station, Platform (C2C)
Southchurch	❯	Southchurch Hall, Woodgrange Drive Southchurch Park, Liftsan Way White Horse, Southchurch Road (Private)
Southend	❯	Dalmatia Road, nr. Southchurch Road Marine Parade, opp. The Ship Pitmans Close Priory Park, Victoria Avenue Seaway Car Park, Queensway (M&F) Pier Gardens (8.00-dusk) (Private) The Royals Shopping Centre (Private) Victoria Circus Shopping Centre (Private) Debenhams Store, The Royals (Debenhams) Southend Central Station, Concourse (C2C) Southend Victoria Station (NX East Anglia) The Bell, Southend Arterial Road (Private) Nandos, 24 London Road (Nandos) Varsity, Chichester Road (Barracuda) Student Union, Elmer Approach (University of Essex)

	Mecca Bingo, Greyhound Shopping Park (Mecca)
	Odeon Cinema (Odeon)
	Roots Hall Stadium (Southend Untd)
Thorpe Bay ❯	Thorpe Esplanade (Apr-October)
Westcliff ❯	London Road/Hamlet Court Road
	Western Esplanade, by Café

STEVENAGE

Stevenage ❯	Fairlands Valley Park, Sailing Centre
	Town Square
	Stevenage Station, Concourse (Capital Connect)
	Nandos, Kings Way (Nandos)
	Nandos, Kings Way (Nandos)
	Standard Bearer, The Plaza (JDW)
	The Standing Order, High Street (JDW)

SUFFOLK COASTAL

Aldeburgh ❯	Fort Green
	Moot Hall
	West Lane
Bawdsey ❯	The Ferry
Blythburgh ❯	Toby's Walks Picnic Site (Suffolk CC) [Summer 2010]
Dunwich ❯	Dunwich Beach
	Dunwich Heath, Coastguard Cottages (National Trust)
Felixstowe ❯	Bathtap, Bath Hill
	Beach Station Road (Daytime)
	Crescent Road Car Park [Planned]
	The Dip
	Golf Road Car Park
	Langer Park (Summer)
	Manor Road Car Park
	Ranelagh Road Car Park (Daytime)
	Spa Pavilion
	Town Hall

Framlingham ❯ Crown & Anchor Lane

Leiston ❯ Dinsdale Road (Daytime) (Parish Council)
Sizewell Road (Daytime)

Martlesham ❯ Red Lion, Main Road (Private)

Orford ❯ Quay Street Car Park (Parish Council)

Saxmundham ❯ Market Place

Saxtead ❯ The Green

Sizewell Beach ❯ Car Park

Thorpeness ❯ The Mere

Walberswick ❯ Village

Wickham Market ❯ Crafers Car Park (Daytime)

Woodbridge ❯ Brook Street (Daytime)
Elmhurst Park (Parish Council)
Jetty Lane
Station Road (Daytime)

TENDRING

Brightlingsea ❯ Promenade Way Car Park
Station Road
Waterside

Clacton ❯ High Street Car Park
Lower Promenade, Ambleside (Easter-Oct)
Lower Promenade, West Greensward
Magdalen Green, Old Road/Coppins Road
Rosemary Road, opp. The Grove
Westcliff, Middle Promenade, nr. Pier
Clacton Station (NX East Anglia)
McDonalds, Pier Avenue (Private)
Moon & Starfish, Marine Parade East (JDW)
Flicks Cinema, Pier Avenue (Private)
Gala Bingo, Pier Avenue (Private)

Dovercourt ❯ Low Road Playing Field
Milton Road Car Park

		Wick Lane, nr. Swimming Pool (May-Oct)
Frinton	❯	Esplanade, opp. Connaught Avenue
		Greensward, Kiosk (May-Oct)
		Lower Promenade, opp. Cambridge Road
		Old Way
Harwich	❯	by High Lighthouse, opp. George Street
Holland-on-Sea	❯	Holland Gap, nr. Car Park
		Ipswich Road, nr. Car Park
		Middle Promenade, opp. Queensway
		(May-Oct)
		Roaring Donkey, Holland Road (Greene King)
Jaywick	❯	Meadow Way/Tamarisk Way
Manningtree	❯	Market Site, Brook Street
Parkeston	❯	Harwich Int. Station, Platform 1 (NX East Anglia)
Walton-on-the-Naze	❯	Coronation Car Park, Princes Esplanade
		(May-Oct)
		Jubilee Beach, Lower Promenade (May-Oct)
		Mill Lane
		Walton-on-Naze Station (NX East Anglia)
		Walton Pier (Private)

THREE RIVERS

Rickmansworth	❯	Aquadrome, Frogmoor Lane (daytime)
		The Pennsylvanian, High Street (JDW)

THURROCK

Chafford Hundred	❯	Chafford Hundred Station, Booking Hall (C2C)
Grays	❯	Civic Hall (Hall hrs)
		Thameside Theatre (Theatre hrs)
		Grays Community Resource Centre (CP)
		Grays Station, Platform 1 (C2C)
		Woodview Campus (Thurrock & Basildon College)
Lakeside	❯	Debenhams Store (Debenhams)
		Old Orleans (Private)
		Nandos, Lakeside Pavilion (Nandos)

Stanford-le-Hope	❯	Stanford Base, The Sorrells (CP)
Tilbury	❯	Tilbury Town Station, Platform 1 (C2C)
West Thurrock M25	❯	Thurrock Services, J30/31 M25 (Moto)

UTTLESFORD

Saffron Walden ❯ The Common Car Park
Swan Meadow
Library (Library hrs) (Essex CC)
The Temeraire, High Street (JDW)

Stansted Airport ❯ Terminal, Airside by Frankie & Bennies (BAA)
Terminal, Airside by Wetherspoons (BAA)
Terminal, Landside by O'Neills (BAA)

Stansted Mountfitchet ❯ Lower Street Car Park

WATFORD

Watford ❯ Charter Place
Cheslyn House, Nascoltwood Rd (Office hrs)
Holywell Community Centre (Centre hrs)
North Watford Cemetery (Cemetery hrs)
Orbital Community Centre, Garston (Centre hrs)
Watford Colosseum, Town Hall (Hall hrs)
Watford Leisure Centre (2) (Centre hrs)
Harlequin Shopping Centre (Private)
Watford Junction Station, Concourse
(London Midland)
Bar Nazdarovya, 135 The Parade (Private)
Café Maximo Bar, High Street (Private)
Caffe Nero, High Street (Caffe Nero)
Chicago Rock Café, The Parade (Private)
Colombia Press, The Parade (JDW)
Destiny Night Club, The Parade (Private)
Essex Arms, Langley Way (Private)
The Flag, Station Road (Private)
Jongleurs, High Street (Private)
Moon Under Water, High Street (JDW)
Nando's, The Parade (Nandos)
Old Orleans, Elton Way (Private)
O'Neills, The Parade (M&B)
Reflex, The Parade (Private)
Revolution, High Street (Private)

The Southern Cross, Langley Road (Private)
Sportz Academy, The Parade (Private)
Vicarage Road Stadium (Watford FC)

WAVENEY

Beccles ❯ Blyburgate Car Park
Hungate Car Park

❯ Yacht Station, The Quay

Bungay ❯ Priory Lane

Halesworth ❯ Thoroughfare Car Park

Kessingland ❯ Church Road
Heathland Beach Caravan Park (Private)
White House Beach Caravan Club Site
(Caravan Club)

Lowestoft ❯ Gordon Road
Jubilee Parade North, South Beach (Summer)
Kensington Gardens, A12
Kirkley Cemetery
Lowestoft Cemetery, Normanston Drive
Pakefield Street
Sparrow's Nest Park (Daytime)
Triangle Market, High Street

Oulton Broad ❯ Nicholas Everitt Park (Daytime)

Southwold ❯ Church Green
The Harbour, Ferry Road
The Pier

WELWYN HATFIELD

Hatfield ❯ Galleria Shopping Centre (2) (Private)
Nandos, 66 Galleria (Nandos)

Welwyn Garden City ❯ Stanborough Lakes, North
Stanborough Lakes, South
Howard Centre (Private)
Commons Wood Caravan Club Site
(Caravan Club)

EAST MIDLANDS

AMBER VALLEY

Alfreton ❯ Bus Station, Severn Square
Rogers Lane
Cemetery, Rogers Lane (8.00-16.30)
Wagon & Horses, King Street (JDW)

Ambergate ❯ Derby Road, A6/A610 junction

Belper ❯ Belper Cemetery (Cemetery hrs)
Bridge Street/Matlock Road, A6 Triangle
River Gardens, Matlock Road
Strutt Street

Codnor ❯ Market Place

Crich ❯ Browns Hill

Duffield ❯ Bridge Inn, Mareney Road (Marstons)

Heage ❯ Eagle Street

Heanor ❯ Market Place
Red Lion, Derby Road (JDW)

Holloway ❯ Church Street

Lea Brooks ❯ Cemetery (Cemetery hrs)

Ripley ❯ Grosvenor Road
Market Place
Red Lion, Market Place (JDW)

Somercotes ❯ Market Place
Sherwood Street Recreation Ground (8.00-16.30)

South Wingfield ❯ Market Place

ASHFIELD

Hucknall ❯ Market Place, Ogle Street
Bowman, Nottingham Road (Private)
Pilgrim Oak, High Street (JDW)

Huthwaite	❯	Columbia Street
Kirkby-in-Ashfield	❯	Station Street, Nags Head Street
Sutton-in-Ashfield	❯	Idlewells Shopping Centre (Private) The Picture House, Fox Street (JDW)

BASSETLAW

Blyth A1(M)	❯	Blyth Services, A1M/A614 (Moto)
Clumber Park	❯	Near Visitor Centre (National Trust) Cricket Ground (National Trust) Caravan Club Site (Caravan Club)
Retford	❯	Bus Station waiting room (Station hrs) Chancery Lane (Shopping hrs) Chapelgate (Shopping hrs) Retford Station, Platform 1 (East Coast) Broadstone (Private) Dominie Cross, Grove Street (JDW) Litten Tree, Chapelgate (Private) Top House, Market Place (Private)
Worksop	❯	Gateford Road (Shopping hrs) Park Street, Market (Shopping hrs) Priory Shopping Centre (Shopping hrs) The Crossing Centre, Victoria Ave (Private) Worksop Station (Northern Rail) Half Moon (Private) Liquorice Gardens, Newcastle Street (JDW) Litten Tree, Victoria Square (Private) Lock Keeper (Private) Three Legged Stool (Private) Top House (Private) White Lion (Private)

BLABY

Blaby	❯	John's Court, Waitrose Car Park
Glen Parva	❯	Glen Parva Manor, The Ford (Marstons)
Kirby Muxloe	❯	Castle Hotel, Main Street (Private)

BOLSOVER

Bolsover ❯ Cavendish Walk (Daytime, Mon-Sat)

BOSTON

Boston ❯ Cattle Market Car Park, Bargate
Central Park (Park hrs)
Lincoln Lane
Market Place (Daytime)
Moon Under Water, High Street (JDW)

Leverton ❯ Picnic Area, off A52 (M&F)

BROXTOWE

Beeston ❯ Beeston Fields Recreation Ground
Broadgate Park, High Road
Bus Station
Leyton Crescent Recreation Ground
Weirfields Recreation Ground, Canal Side
Last Post, Chilwell Road (JDW)

Chilwell ❯ Charlton Arms, High Road (Private)

Eastwood ❯ Nottingham Road, by Library

Kimberley ❯ Main Street

Stapleford ❯ Ilkeston Road Recreation Ground
Queen Elizabeth Park, Toton Lane
The Roach

Toton ❯ Manor Farm Recreation Ground

CHARNWOOD

Anstey ❯ The Nook Car Park (8.00-18.00)

Barrow-on-Soar ❯ High Street Car Park (8.00-18.00)

Birstall ❯ Stonehill Avenue (8.00-18.00)

Loughborough ❯
Beehive Lane
Biggin Street
Charnwood Water (8.00-18.00)
Granby Street
Market Yard (8.00-18.00)
Outwoods Park (Park Events)
Queens Park (8.00-18.00)
Southfield Park (Park Events)
Sainsbury's Store, Greenclose La. (Sainsbury)
Amber Rooms, The Rushes (JDW)
Moon & Bell, Wards End (JDW)

Markfield M1 ❯ Leicester Services, A50/M1 (Moto)

Quorn ❯ Station Road (8.00-18.00)

Shepshed ❯ Hallcroft (8.00-18.00)

Sileby ❯ King Street (8.00-18.00)

Syston ❯ Melton Road (8.00-18.00)

Woodhouse Eaves ❯ Main Street (8.00-18.00)

CHESTERFIELD

Brimington ❯ High Street

Chesterfield ❯
Beetwell Street Coach Station
New Square, Market Hall Basement
(Mon-Sat, daytime)
Pavements Centre (Mon-Sat, daytime)
Queens Park, North Lodge (Daytime)
Vicar Lane Shopping Centre (Private)
Sainsbury's Store, Rother Way (Sainsbury)
Chesterfield Station, Platform 1 (E. Midlands Trains)
Portland Hotel, West Bars (JDW)
Spa Lane Vaults, St Marys Gate (JDW)
Yates's Bar, Burlington Street (Yates)

Hollingwood ❯ Hollingwood Hotel, Private Drive (Marstons)

Newbold ❯ Holmebrook Valley Park (dawn-dusk)

Old Whittington	❯	by Swanick Memorial Hall, High Street
Poolsbrook	❯	Poolsbrook County Park, Fan Rd (dawn-dusk)
Somersall	❯	Somersall Park, Somersall Lane
Staveley	❯	Market Place Car Park
Tapton	❯	Tapton Park (Dawn-dusk)
Whittington Moor	❯	Duke Street, off Sheffield Road

CORBY

Corby	❯	Boating Lake, Cottingham Road (Park hrs)
		Market Walk, Queens Square (Private)
		Willow Place Shopping Centre (Private)
		Samuel Lloyd, Rockingham Rd/Gretton Rd (JDW)
		Civic Hub Shopping Complex [Planned] (CP)
		Swimming Complex [Planned] (CP)
East Carlton	❯	East Carlton Countryside Park (Park hrs)

DAVENTRY

Daventry	❯	Daventry Country Park, Welton Road
		New Street, by Bus Station
		Queen of Hearts, Ashby Fields (Marstons)
		Saracen's Head, Brook Street (JDW)

DERBY

Allenton	❯	Allenton Market (Market days)
Derby	❯	Arboretum, Rosehill Street end
		Bold Lane Car Park
		Chaddesdon Park, Chaddesdon Lane
		Darley Park, nr. Café
		Darley Playing Fields
		Markeaton Park, nr Craft Village
		Munday Play Centre
		Quad, Market Place (Gallery hrs)
		Rowditch Recreation Ground
		The Spot, London Road/Osmaston Road

East Midlands

Victoria Street
Derby Station, Platforms 1 & 4 (E Midlands Trains)
Babington Arms, Babington Lane (JDW)
Fat Cats, Friar Gate (Private)
Nandos, 15 Market Place (Nandos)
Old Orleans, Pride Parkway (Private)
Revolution, Wardwick (Private)
Soda Bar, Friar Gate (Private)
Standing Order, Irongate (JDW)
Varsity, Friar Gate (Private)
Walkabout, Market Place (Private)
Yates's Bar, Irongate (Yates)
Pride Park Stadium (Derby County FC)

Littleover ❯ Burton Road Shops

DERBYSHIRE DALES

Ashbourne ❯ Bus Station
Recreation Ground
Shaw Croft Car Park
Mappleton Lane Car Park (Peak District NP)

Ashford-in-the-Water ❯ -

Bakewell ❯ Agricultural Business Centre (Centre hrs)
Granby Road
Recreation Ground
Riverside

Baslow ❯ -
Chatsworth Park Caravan Club Site
(Caravan Club)

Bradwell ❯ -

Cromford ❯ Memorial Gardens

Darley Dale ❯ Station Road

Dovedale ❯ Dovedale Car Park (Peak District NP)

Eyam ❯ -

Hartington ❯ -

Hathersage	❯	-
Kirk Ireton	❯	Blackwall Plantation Caravan Club Site (Caravan Club)
Matlock	❯	Artists Corner Bus Station Hall Leys Play Area Hall Leys Roadside The Crown, Crown Square (JDW)
Matlock Bath	❯	North Parade Pavilion
Middleton-by-Youlgreave		-
Middleton Top	❯	Picnic Site (Derbys CC)
Monsal	❯	Monsal Head
Over Haddon	❯	-
Parsley Hay	❯	Cycle Hire Centre, A515 (Private)
Thorpe	❯	-
Tideswell	❯	- Tideswell Dale Car Park (Peak District NP)
Winster	❯	-
Wirksworth	❯	Barmcote Croft Car Park

EAST LINDSEY

Anderby	❯	Anderby Creek
Burgh Le Marsh	❯	Market Place
Chapel St Leonards	❯	Bus Station, Sea Road (Daytime) Chapel Point (Easter-October) Trunch Lane (Easter-October)
Conningsby	❯	Car Park, off High Street

East Midlands

Horncastle ◐ St Lawrence Street

Huttoft ◐ Huttoft Bank

Ingoldmells ◐ Sea Lane, The Point (Daytime)
Vickers Point
Village Centre (Daytime)

Louth ◐ Bus Station, Church Street (Daytime)
Eastgate, by Market Hall (Daytime)
Hubbards Hill (Daytime)
Newmarket

Mablethorpe ◐ Bohemia (Easter-Oct & weekends)
Central Promenade (Daytime)
Dunes Gardens, Quebec Road (Daytime)
Golf Road (Easter-Oct & weekends)
North End (Easter-Oct & weekends)
Park Square (6.00-20.00)
Queens Park (Easter-Oct & weekends)
Seacroft Road Bus Station (Easter-October)
South Promenade (Easter-Oct)

North Somercotes ◐ Playing Field

North Thoresby ◐ - (Daytime)

Saltfleet ◐ Sea Lane (Daytime)

Skegness ◐ Briar Way (Daytime) CP
Lumley Square
North Parade
Princes Parade (Easter-October)
Scarborough Esplanade, under Pier (Easter-Oct)
Tower Esplanade
Tower Gardens (6.00-20.00)
Winthorpe Avenue
Skegness Station (E. Midlands Trains)
Red Lion, Roman Bank (JDW)
Embassy Centre, Upper Foyer (Private)

Spilsby ◐ Market Place

Sutton-on-Sea ◐ by Sandilands Golf Course (Daytime)
Sutton Pleasure Gardens (Daytime)
Hawthorn Farm Caravan Club Site (Caravan Club)

Tetney	❯	by Village Hall (Daytime)
Trusthorpe	❯	Bohemia (Easter-Oct & weekends)
Wainfleet	❯	Brooks Walk (6.00-20.00)
Winthorpe	❯	Sandfield, Roman Bank
Woodhall Spa	❯	Jubilee Park (Easter-October) Spa Road (Daytime)
Wragby	❯	Market Place (Daytime)

EAST NORTHAMPTONSHIRE

Higham Ferrers	❯	Wharf Road (daytime)
Irthlingborough	❯	High Street (daytime)
Oundle	❯	St Osyth's Lane (daytime)
Raunds	❯	Marshals Road (Town Council)
Rushden	❯	Duck Street (daytime) Newton Road (daytime)
Thrapston	❯	Oundle Road (daytime)

EREWASH

Borrowash	❯	Victoria Avenue, Supermarket Car Park
Breaston	❯	Blind Lane
Draycott	❯	Markets Street/Derby Street
Ilkeston	❯	Gallows Inn Market Place, Bath Street Station Road Moon & Sixpence, Woodland Ave (Private) The Observatory, Market Place (JDW)
Long Eaton	❯	Hall Grounds Orchard Street Long Eaton Station

East Midlands

East Midlands

Market Trader
Trent Lock
West Park Pavilion
Twitchel Inn, Howitt Street (JDW)

Sandiacre	❯	Longmoor Lane
Sawley	❯	Bell Inn, Tamworth Road (Private)
Trowell M1	❯	Trowell Services, J25/26 M1 (Moto)

GEDLING

Arnold	❯	Arnot Hill Park (Kiosk hrs)
		Burntstump Park Car Park (8.00-17.00)
		Front Street
		King George V Park (8.00-Dusk)
		Redhill Cemetery (Cemetery hrs)
		Wood Street (8.00-18.00)
		Methodist Church, Market Place (Church)
		Burnt Stump, Burnt Stump Hill (Marstons)
		The Ernehale, Nottingham Road (JDW)
		Friar Tuck, Gedling Road (Private)
Bestwood Country Park	❯	Alexandra Lodge (Notts CC)
Burton Joyce	❯	Wheatsheaf Inn, Main Street (Private)
Calverton	❯	St Wilfreds Square (8.00-17.00)
Carlton	❯	Albert Avenue
		Cavendish Road, nr. Cemetery (8.00-Dusk)
Gedling	❯	Chesterfield Arms, Main Road (Private)
Mapperley	❯	Haywood Road Car Park
		Woodthorpe Top, Woodthorpe Rd (JDW)
Netherfield	❯	Morris Street Car Park
Ravenshead	❯	Milton Court Shopping Precinct
Stoke Bardolph	❯	Ferry Boat Inn (Private)

HARBOROUGH

Broughton Astley  Orchard Road Car Park

Great Bowden Recreation Ground

Little Bowden Recreation Ground

Lutterworth George Street Car Park

Market Harborough The Commons Car Park
Riverside Walk, St Mary's Place
Welland Park, Welland Park Road
Market Harborough Station, Plastform 1
(E Midlands Trains)
Peacock, St Mary's Place (Marstons)
The Sugar Loaf, High Street (JDW)

HIGH PEAK

Bamford Main Road

Buxton Market Place (8.00-17.00)
Pavilion Gardens Boating Lake (Daytime)
Pavilion Gardens Car Park (Daytime)
Sylvan Car Park
Grin Low Country Park (Derbys CC)
Wye Bridge House, Fairfield Road (JDW)

		Grin Low Caravan Club Site (Caravan Club)
Castleton	🔘	Losehill Caravan Club Site (Caravan Club)
Chinley	🔘	Green Lane
Edale	🔘	Car Park
Glossop	🔘	Manor Park Market Place Norfolk Arms, High Street (Private)
Hadfield	🔘	Platt Street (8.00-18.00)
Hayfield	🔘	Hayfield Countryside Centre Sett Valley Trail Car Park (Derbys CC) Bowden Bridge car park (Peak District NP)
Hope	🔘	Castleton Road Car Park
New Mills	🔘	High Street
Whaley Bridge	🔘	Market Street

HINCKLEY & BOSWORTH

Barwell	🔘	Top Town, Shilton Road (Daytime)
Burbage	🔘	Lychgate Lane
Earl Shilton	🔘	Wood Street
Hinckley	🔘	Ashby Road Cemetery (Cemetery hrs) Hollycroft Park (Park hrs) Leisure Centre, Coventry Road (Centre hrs) Station Road (Daytime) Baron of Hinckley, Regent Street (JDW) Hinckley Knights, Watling Street (Private)
Market Bosworth	🔘	Back Lane
Newbold Verdon	🔘	Methodist Church Car Park (Church)

KETTERING

Burton Latimer	🔘	Churchill Way Car Park

Desborough ❯ Buckwell Close

Kettering ❯ Dalkeith Place
Ebenezer Place
Rockingham Park, Park Road
Newlands Shopping Centre (Private)
Kettering Station, Platform 1 (E Midlands Trains)
Earl of Dalkeith, Dalkeith Place (JDW)
Nandos, Kettering Business Park (Nandos)

Rothwell ❯ Squires Hill

LEICESTER

Leicester ❯ Belgrave Road, by Flyover
Clarendon Gardens, by Library
Cossington Street, by Recreation Ground
East Park Road, Spinney Hill Park
Foundary Square, Belgrave Gate
Infirmary Square
Knighton Lane East, opp. Leisure Centre
Welford Road, Nelson Mandela Park
Thurcaston Road
Leicester Station, Platforms 2 & 4
(E. Midlands Trains)
Corn Exchange, Market Place (JDW)
Gynsills, Leicester Road, Glenfield (Private)
Heathley Park, Groby Road (Private)
High Cross, High Street (JDW)
Jongleurs, Granby Street (Private)
Last Plantagenet, Granby Street (JDW)
Nandos, Freemans Leisure Park (Nandos)
Nandos, Granby Street (Nandos)
Nandos, Highcross (Nandos)
Owl & Pussycat, Melton Road (Private)
Varsity, Friar Lane (Barracuda)
Varsity, London Road (Barracuda)
Walkabout, Granby Street (Private)
Yates's Bar, Belvoir Street (Yates)
Walkers Stadium (Leics City FC)

LINCOLN

Lincoln ❯ Castle Square
City Bus Station

Hartsholme Country Park, Visitor Centre (Daytime)
Lucy Tower Street
Tentercroft Street
Westgate, nr. Union Road
Waterside Shopping Centre (Private)
Lincoln Station, Platform 5 (E. Midlands Trains)
The Forum, Silver Street (JDW)
Nandos, Brayford Wharf North (Nandos)
The Ritz, High Street (JDW)
Slug & Lettuce, Brayford Wharf (Private)
Square Sail, Brayford Wharf North (JDW)
Varsity, Guildhall Street (Barracuda)
Walkabout, High Street (Private)
Yates's Bar, High Street (Yates)

MANSFIELD

Mansfield ❯

Bus Station
Four Seasons Shopping Centre
Mansfield Town Hall, Market Place
St Johns Street
Mansfield Station (E. Midlands Trains)
Courthouse, Market Place (JDW)
Ravensdale, Sherwood Hall Rd (Marstons)
Rufford, Chesterfield Rd South (Marstons)
Rushley, Nottingham Road (Marstons)
Swan, Church Street (Marstons)
Widow Frost, Leeming Street (JDW)
Yates's Bar, Leeming Street (Yates)
Gala Bingo, Albert Street (Gala)

Mansfield Woodhouse ❯

Rose Lane

Warsop ❯

High Street Car Park

MELTON

Melton Mowbray ❯

Cattle Market (Market Days)
Park Lane
St Mary's Way
Kettleby Cross, Wilton Road (JDW)

NEWARK & SHERWOOD

Bilsthorpe ❯ Copper Beech, Kirklington Road (Private)

Clipstone ❯ Vicar Water Country Park Visitor Centre (Daytime)

Edwinstowe ❯ Mansfield Road, by Village Hall
Sherwood Forest Country Park Visitor Centre (Notts CC)

Gunthorpe ❯ Anchor Inn, Main Street (Private)
Unicorn Hotel, Gunthorpe Bridge (Private)

Kelham ❯ Kelham Hall Civic Suite (Suite hrs)

Laxton ❯ Dovecote Inn Car Park (Dawn-Dusk)

Lowdham ❯ Southwell Rd/Main Street

New Balderton ❯ The Grove, London Road (Private)

Newark ❯ Castle Grounds, Gilstrap Building (Daytime)
London Road Car Park (Daytime)
Tolney Lane, Riverside Park
Buttermarket (Private)
Newark Northgate Station, Platforms 1&3 (East Coast)
Atrium, Castle Gate (Private)
Sir John Arderne, Church Street (JDW)

Ollerton ❯ Sherwood Heath Inf. Centre (Centre hrs)
Rufford Country Park, The Abbey (Notts CC)

Rainworth ❯ Robin Hood, Southwell Road East (Private)

Rufford ❯ Rose Cottage, Old Rufford Road (Private)

Southwell ❯ Church Street Car Park

NORTH EAST DERBYSHIRE

Ashover ❯ Crispin Inn, Church Street (Private)

Clay Cross ❯ Market Street (Parish Council)

Dronfield 🡢 Cliff Park, Calleywhite Lane (Town Council)

Grassmoor 🡢 Boot & Shoe, North Wingfield Road (Private)

NORTH EAST LINCOLNSHIRE

Cleethorpes 🡢 Boating Lake, off Kings Road
Kingsway, nr. Leisure Centre
St Peter's Avenue, off Car Park
Sea Road
Cleethorpes Station (Transpennine)
The Wellow, Kings Road (Private)
Pleasure Island (Private)

Grimsby 🡢 Garibaldi Street (M&F) (Mon-Sat 8.30-17.30)
Market Hall (Mon-Sat 8.30-17.30)
Freshney Place Shopping Centre (Private)
Bradley Inn, Bradley Crossroads (Private)
DN31, Victoria Street (Private)
Ice Barque, Frederick Ward Way (JDW)
The Parity, Old Market Place (Barracuda)
Walkabout, Riverhead (Private)
Yarborough Hotel, Bethlehem St. (JDW)
Yates's Bar, Riverhead (Yates)
Great Grimsby Swimming Pool, Scartho Rd
(Private)
Grimsby Leisure Centre, Cromwell Rd (Private)

Immingham 🡢 Kennedy Way, off Car Park

Stallingborough 🡢 Green Man, Station Road (Private)

Waltham 🡢 Waltham Windmill & Grounds
Kings Head, High Street (Private)

NORTH KESTEVEN

Sleaford 🡢 Money's Yard, Carre Street (8.00-17.00)
Packhorse Inn, Northgate (JDW)

Whisby 🡢 Whisby Nature Park, Visitor Centre (Private)

NORTH LINCOLNSHIRE

Barton-on-Humber ❯ Baysgarth Park, Brigg Road
Humber Bridge Viewing Area
Market Place

Belton ❯ Picnic Area, off A161

Brigg ❯ Barnard Avenue/Bigby High Road
Cary Lane
Elsham Country Park, Car Park (Private)

Epworth ❯ Chapel Street Car Park

Haxey ❯ Vinehall Road/High Street

Owston Ferry ❯ High Street

Scunthorpe ❯ Ashby High Street, Car Park
Dunstall Street Car Park
Frodingham Road/Doncaster Road
Library Square MSCP
Normanby Hall Country Park
Normanby Hall Country Park, Car Park
Parishes MSCP, by Shopmobility
Scunthorpe Station (Transpennine)
Blue Bell Inn, Oswald Road (JDW)
Scunthorpe Bowl, Warren Road (AMF)

NORTH WEST LEICESTERSHIRE

Ashby-de-la-Zouch ❯ Kilwardby Street/Derby Road

Castle Donington ❯ Bus Station, High Street/Delven Lane

Coalville ❯ Market Hall Car Park (Daytime, Mon-Sat)
Monkey Walk, Marlborough Square (JDW)

Donnington Park M1 ❯ Donington Park Services, J23A M1 (Moto)

Ibstock ❯ High Street (Daytime Mon-Sat)

Kegworth ❯ Market Place (Daytime, Mon-Sat)

Measham ❯ High Street (Daytime, Mon-Sat)

| Moira | ❯ | Moira Craft Workshops (Private) |

NORTHAMPTON

Northampton	❯	Abbey Street (7.30-16.00)
		Abington Park, Bowling Green (7.30-16.00)
		Bus Station (7.20-19.20)
		Guildhall, St Giles Square (Office hrs)
		Sheep Street, opp. Mayorhold
		Central Library, Abington Street (Northants CC)
		Grosvenor Shopping Centre (Private)
		Peacock Place Shopping Centre (Private)
		Weston Favel Shopping Centre (Private)
		Debenhams Store, The Drapery (Debenhams)
		Northampton Station, Booking Hall (London Midland)
		Ask, St Giles Square (Private)
		Auctioneers, Market Square (Marstons)
		Billing Mill Restaurant, The Causeway (Private)
		Chicago Rock Café, Market Square (Private)
		Cordwainer, The Ridings (JDW)
		Fish Inn, Fish Street (Private)
		Fox & Hounds, Harborough Rd, Kingsthorpe (Private)
		Frog & Fiddler, Harborough Road (Private)
		Hungry Horse, Sixfields Leisure Park (Private)
		Lloyds Bar, Abington Street (JDW)
		Moon on the Square, Market Square (JDW)
		N.B's, Bridge Street (Private)
		Queen Eleanor, London Road, Wootton (Private)
		Toad at Sol Central, Sol Central (Private)
		White Elephant, Kingley Park Terrace (Private)
		Yates's Bar, The Ridings (Yates)
		Billings Aquadrome (Private)
		Tenpin 10, Sixfields Leisure Park (Private)

NOTTINGHAM

Nottingham	❯	Duke Street, Bulwell (7.00-18.00)
		Greyhound Street, Market Square (CP)
		Gregory Boulevard, Forest Recreation Site
		Gregory Boulevard, Hyson Green (7.00-18.00)
		Ken Martin Leisure Centre, Bulwell (CP)
		Spondon Street, Sherwood
		Trent Bridge, Victoria Embankment

Wollaton Hall, Wollaton Park (CP)
Castle College, Carlton Road Centre (College)
Debenhams Store, Long Row (Debenhams)
Nottingham Station, Platforms 1&5
(E. Midlands Trains)
Broxtowe Inn, Nuthall Rd, Cinderhill (Private)
Company Inn, Castle Wharf (JDW)
Fox, Valley Road, Basford (Private)
Grove Castle Hotel, Castle Boulevard (Private)
Ha! Ha! Bar, Weekday Cross (Private)
Jongleurs, Castle Wharf (Private)
Joseph Else, Market Square (JDW)
KFC, Lower Parliament Street (KFC)
Liit Nottingham, Market Street (Private)
Lloyds Bar, Carlton Street (JDW)
Nandos, Angel Row, Market Sq (Nandos)
Nandos, Redfield Way, Lenton (Nandos)
Old Dog & Partridge, Lower Parliament St (Private)
Pit & Pendulum, Victoria Street (Private)
Roebuck Inn, St James Street (JDW)
Varsity, Peel Street (Barracuda)
Walkabout, Friar Lane (Private)
Willoughby Arms, Wollaton (Private)
Gala Bingo, Hucknell Road (Gala)
Gala Bingo, St Ann's Well Road (Gala)

OADBY & WIGSTON

Great Glen ❯ Yews, London Road (Private)

Oadby ❯ East Street Car Park
Horse & Hounds, Glen Rise (Private)
Lord Keeper of the Great Seal", The Parade (JDW)

South Wigston ❯ Blaby Road

Wigston ❯ Junction Road
Peace Memorial Park
William Wygston, Leicester Road (JDW)

RUSHCLIFFE

Ruddington ❯ Millers, Loughborough Road (Private)

Wilford ❯ Ferry Inn (Private)

| West Bridgford | ❯ | Bridgford Park, Central Avenue (Dawn-dusk) |

RUTLAND

| Oakham | ❯ | Church Street Car Park (7.00-18.00)
John Street, Westgate Car Park (7.00-18.00) |
| Uppingham | | Market Place (7.00-18.00) |

SOUTH DERBYSHIRE

Etwall	❯	Eggington Road (Dawn-dusk)
Melbourne	❯	Leisure Centre (Private)
Overseal	❯	Woodsville Road (Dawn-dusk)
Repton	❯	Bulls Head, High Street (Private)
Shardlow	❯	Clock Warehouse (Marstons)
Swadlincote	❯	Bus Park, Civic Way (Dawn-dusk) East End Car Park (Dawn-dusk) Sir Nigel Gresley, Market Street (JDW)
Ticknall	❯	Ingleby Lane (Dawn-dusk) Calke Abbey, Restaurant Yard (Nat. Trust)
Willington	❯	Canal Bridge (Dawn-dusk)

SOUTH HOLLAND

Crowland	❯	Town Centre West Street
Donnington	❯	Park Lane, off A54
Holbeach	❯	Church Street
Long Sutton	❯	West Street
Spalding	❯	Ayscoughfee Gardens (8.00-dusk) Bus Station, Winfrey Avenue Sheepmarket (8.00-18.00)

Vine Street
Ivy Wall, New Road (JWD)

Sutton Bridge ❯ Bridge Road, off A17

SOUTH KESTEVEN

Bourne ❯ South Street (Town Council)

Gonerby Moor A1 ❯ Grantham North Services, A1 (Moto)

Grantham ❯ Abbey Gardens
Arnoldfield Playing Field (Apr-Sept, 9.00-19.00)
Conduit Lane
London Road
George Shopping Centre (Private)
Grantham Station, Platform 1 (East Coast)
Tollemache Inn, St Peter's Hill (JDW)
Gala Bingo, Trent Road (Gala)

Market Deeping ❯ The Precinct (Town Council)

Stamford ❯ Red Lion Square

SOUTH NORTHAMPTONSHIRE

Brackley ❯ Market Place

Stoke Bruerne ❯ Navigation, Bridge Road (Marstons)

Towcester ❯ Sponne Precinct Car Park, Richmond Road

WELLINGBOROUGH

Finedon ❯ Recreation Ground, Wellingborough Road

Sywell ❯ Overstone Manor, Ecton Lane (Private)

Wellingborough ❯ Bassetts Park
Commercial Way MSCP (2) (7.30-17.30)
Embankment
Market Square (7.30-18.00)
Swanspool Gardens (7.30-dusk)
Wellingborough Station, Platform 1
(E Midlands Trains)

Red Well, Silver Street (JDW)
Wellingborough Bowl, Victoria Retail Pk (AMF)

WEST LINDSEY

Caistor ❯ Town Hall Car Park

Gainsborough ❯ Corporation Yard, Bridge Street
Roseway Car Park
Whittons Gardens, Caskgate Street
Sweyn Forkbeard, Silver Street (JDW)
Roseway Car Park
Whittons Gardens, Caskgate Street
Sweyn Forkbeard, Silver Street (JDW)

Market Rasen ❯ John Street
Willingham Wood, by Café, A631

Saxilby ❯ Bridge Street

East Midlands

WEST MIDLANDS

BIRMINGHAM

Acocks Green ❯
Westley Road, by Laffertys
Spread Eagle, Warwick Road (JDW)

Aston ❯
Villa Park (Aston Villa FC)

Birmingham City Centre ❯
Central Library (Library hours)
Hurst Street/Queensway
Newton Street
Steelhouse Lane
Stephenson Place
Waterloo Street
Millennium Point, Curzon Street (Private)
Pallasades Shopping Centre (Private)
Pavilion Central, by Food Court (Private)
Moor Street Station (Chiltern Railway)
New Street Station, Concourse (Network Rail)
Briar Rose, Bennetts Hill (JDW)
Dragon Inn, Hurst Street (JDW)
Figure of Eight, Broad Street (JDW)
Ha! Ha! Bar, The Mailbox (Private)
The Hornet, Alum Rock Road (JDW)
Jongleurs, Quayside Tower (Private)
Malt House, Brindley Place (Private)
Nandos, The Mailbox (Nandos)
Nandos, R2 The New Bullring (Nandos)
Old Joint Stock, Temple Row West (Fullers)
Old Orleans, Broad Street (Private)
Soloman Cutler, Regency Wharf (JDW)
Square Peg, Corporation Street (JDW)
Toad at the Bullring, Hurst Street (Private)
Walkabout, Regency Wharf (Private)
Wetherspoons, Paradise Place (JDW)
Yates's Bar, Corporation Street (Yates)
Gala Casino, Hill Street (Gala)

Cotteridge ❯
Pershore Road, opp Watford Road

Edgbaston
Five Ways Island
Five Ways Station (London Midland)
University Station (London Midland)
Nandos, 5A Five Ways Leisure Centre (Nandos)

		County Ground (Warwickshire CCC)
Erdington	❯	Wilton Road/High Street
		Charlie Hall, Barnabas Road (JDW) Gala Bingo, Streetly Road (Gala)
Handsworth	❯	Baker Street, off Soho Road
Harborne	❯	High Street Old House at Home,Lordswood Road (Private) Varsity, High Street (Barracuda) Gala Bingo, High Street (Gala)
Highgate	❯	Gooch Street
Hockley	❯	Vyse Street, Jewellery Quarter Jewellery Quarter Statiom (London Midland)
Kings Heath	❯	Vicarage Road Pear Tree, Alcester Road South (JDW)
Kings Norton	❯	Kings Norton Station (London Midland)
Kingstanding	❯	Kingstanding Road
Longbridge	❯	Longbridge Station (London Midland)
Lozells	❯	Boulton Road Lozells Road/Heathfield Road
Moseley	❯	Alcester Road, by St Marys Row Elizabeth of York, St Mary's Row (JDW)
Nechells	❯	Nandos, Star City (Nandos) Old Orleans, Star City (Private)
Northfield	❯	Church Road Car Park Bournville College, Bristol Rd South (College)
Selly Oak	❯	Bristol Road/Harborne Lane Selly Oak Station (London Midland)
Small Heath	❯	Coventry Road/Regent Park Road
Sparkhill	❯	Stratford Road, Sparkhill Park

Stechford	❯	Pool Way Shopping Centre
Stirchley	❯	Pershore Road, opp Hazlewell Street
Sutton Coldfield	❯	Boldmere Road/Jockey Road The Mall Gracechurch (Private) Bishop Vesey, Boldmere Road (JDW) Boot Inn, Rectory Road (Private) Bottle of Sack, Birmingham Road (JDW)
Walmley	❯	Crawford Street
Weoley Castle	❯	Weoley Castle Road
Wythall	❯	Chapel Lane Caravan Club Site (Caravan Club)
Yardley	❯	Gala Bingo, Swan Centre, Coventry Rd (Gala)

BROMSGROVE

Bromsgrove	❯	Market Street (Daytime) Sanders Park (Park hrs) Golden Cross Hotel, High Street (JDW)
Frankley M5	❯	Frankley Services, J3/4 M5 (Moto)
Rubery	❯	New Road
Upton Warren	❯	Swan Inn, Worcester Road (Private)

CANNOCK CHASE

Cannock	❯	Linford Arms, High Green (JDW) Yates's Bar, High Green (Yates)
Hendesford	❯	Cannock Chase Visitor Centre (Staffs CC)
Rugeley	❯	The Plaza, Horsefair (JDW)

COVENTRY

Ansty	❯	Ansty Arms, Combe Fields Road (Private)
Canley	❯	Neighbourhood Office

Cannon Park	>	De Montfort Way Shopping Centre
Cheylesmore	>	Daventry Road/Cecily Road
Coventry City Centre	>	British Road Transport Museum (Museum hrs)
		Central Library (Library hrs)
		Leigh Mills Car Park, off Hill Street
		Pool Meadow Bus Station (Centro)
		Cathedral Lanes Shopping Centre (Private)
		Lower Precinct Shopping Centre (Private)
		West Orchard Shopping Centre (Private)
		Coventry Station, Platform 1 (Virgin)
		Earl of Mercia, High Street (JDW)
		Flying Standard, Trinity Street (JDW)
		Nandos, Trinity Street (Nandos)
		Old Orleans, The Sky Dome (Private)
		Varsity, Little Park Street (Barracuda)
		Yates's Bar, High Street (Yates)
		Belgrade Theatre (Private)
		Gala Bingo, Radford Road (Gala)
Earlsdon	>	Library, Albany Road
		City Arms, Earlsdon Street (JDW)
Edgwick	>	Edgwick Park, Foleshill Road
Gosford Green	>	Binley Road/Walsgrave Road
Radford	>	Jubilee Crescent Shopping Centre
Tile Hill	>	Tile Hill Station (London Midland)
Walsgrave	>	Nandos, Gielug Way (Nandos)

DUDLEY

Amblecote	>	Sainsbury's Store, Sandringham Way (Sainsbury)
Brierley Hill	>	Little Cottage Street
		Corn Exchange, Amblecote Road (Private)
Coseley	>	Castle Street
Dudley	>	Flood Street Car Park (M&F)
		Market Place

Bus Station, Birmingham Street (Centro)
Full Moon, High Street (JDW)
Nandos, Castlegate (Nandos)
Gala Bingo, Castle Hill (Gala)

Halesowen ❯ Halesowen Bus Station (Centro)
William Shenstone, Queensway (JDW)

Kingswinford ❯ The Cross

Merry Hill ❯ Debenhams Store, Pedmore Road (Debenhams)
Abraham Darby, Merry Hill (JDW)
Bar Edge, Level Street (Private)
Nandos, Food Court (Nandos)
Waterfront Inn, Level Street (JDW)

Netherton ❯ Halesowen Road

Sedgley ❯ Townsend Place
The Clifton, Bull Ring (JDW)

Stourbridge ❯ Court Street, off New Road
Ryemarket
Bus Station, Foster Street (Centro)
Stourbridge Junction Station (London Midland)
Edward Rutland, High Street (JDW)

Wollaston ❯ Meridan Avenue

EAST STAFFORDSHIRE

Barton-under-Needwood Crowberry Lane, off Main Street

Branston ❯ Branston Water Park (Park hrs)
The Gate, Main Street (Private)

Burton-on-Trent ❯ Manor Croft, Market Place
Shobnall Leisure Complex (Centre hrs)
Station Road
Town Hall (Office hrs)
Register Office & Consumer Direct (Office hrs)
(Staffs CC)
Octagon Shopping Centre (Private)
The Albion, Shobnall Road (Marstons)
Barracuda, Station Street (Barracuda)
Cosmopolitan Bar, High Street (Private)

Lord Burton, High Street (JDW)
Wing Wah Restaurant, New Street (Private)
Yates's Bar, High Street (Yates)
Mecca Bingo, Middleway Park (Private)

Rolleston-on-Dove ❯ Spread Eagle, Church Road (M&B)

Stapenhill ❯ Main Street
Crown Inn, Rosildon Road (Private)

Stretton ❯ Mill House, Milford Drive (Private)

Tutbury ❯ Duke Street Car Park
Dog & Partridge, High Street (Private)

Uttoxeter ❯ Bradley Street
Bramshall Road Recreation Ground
Trinity Road Car Park
Old Swan, Market Place (JDW)
Uttoxeter Racecourse Caravan Club Site
(Caravan Club)

Winshill ❯ Berry Hedge Youth Centre (Centre hrs)

HEREFORDSHIRE

Colwell ❯ British Camp

Hereford ❯ Mayford Orchard Shopping Centre (7.30-18.00)
Hereford Leisure Pool (CP)
Tesco Store, Fryzer Court (Tesco)
Hereford Station (Arriva Wales)
Kings Fee, Commercial Road (JDW)

Kington ❯ Mill Street

Ledbury ❯ Church Lane (8.00-18.00)

Leominster ❯ Broad Street Car Park
Central Par Park
Grange (6.00-17.00)
Leominster Leisure Centre (CP)

Moorhampton ❯ Moorhampton Caravan Club Site
(Caravan Club)

Ross-on-Wye	❯	Croft Shopping Centre (8.00-19.00) Red Meadow, Swimming Pool Car Park (6.00-18.00) Wye Street (7,00-17.00) Mail Rooms, Gloucester Road (JDW)
Weobley	❯	Back Lane

LICHFIELD

Burntwood	❯	Sankeys Corner (7.30-17.30) Swan Island (9.00-17.30)
Chasetown	❯	High Street (7.30-17.00)
Lichfield	❯	Bus Station, Birmingham Road (7.00-18.00) Dam Street (9.00-17.30) Friary (8.00-17.30) Swan Road (9.00-17.30) Acorn Inn, Tamworth Street (JDW) Gatehouse, Bird Street (JDW)

MALVERN HILLS

Bransford	❯	Fox Inn, Bransford Court Lane (Private)
Great Malvern	❯	Barnards Green (7.00-19.00) Grange Road (7.00-19.00) Great Malvern Station (London Midland)
Hanley Swan	❯	Blackmore Caravan Club Site (Caravan Club)
Malvern Link	❯	Victoria Pavilion (Town Council)
Tenbury Wells	❯	Teme Street Car Park (7.00-19.00)
Upton-upon-Severn	❯	Hanley Road Car Park High Street

NEWCASTLE-UNDER-LYME

Kidsgrove	❯	Heathcote Street (8.00-18.00)
Newcastle-under-Lyme	❯	Hassell Street Merrial Street

Sainsbury's Store, Liverpool Rd (Sainsbury)
Arnold Machin, Ironmarket (JDW)
Yates's Bar, Ironmarket (Yates)

NORTH WARWICKSHIRE

Atherstone ❯ Bus Station

Coleshill ❯ High Street
Coleshill Parkway Station (London Midland)
Bell Inn, Birmingham Road (Private)

Water Orton Birmingham Road

NUNEATON & BEDWORTH

Bedworth ❯ Civic Hall (Hall hrs)
Chapel Street (9.00-17.30. Mon-Sat)
Market Place (9.00-17.30. Mon-Sat)
Bear & Ragged Staff, King Street (JDW)

Nuneaton ❯ Bus Station
Ropewalk Shopping Centre MSCP (Centre hrs)
Town Hall, Coton Road (Office hrs)
Nuneaton Station (London Midland)
Sainsbury's Store, Vicarage St (Sainsbury)
Felix Holt, Stratford Street (JDW)

REDDITCH

Redditch ❯ Morton Stanley Changing Rooms, Green Lane
Redditch Town Hall, Walter Stranz Sq (Office hrs)
Threadneedle House, Alcester St (Office hrs)
Woodrow Centre One Stop Shop, Studley Road
Kingfisher Shopping Centre (5) (Private)
Foxlydiate, Birchfield Road (Private)
Rising Sun, Alcester Street (JDW)
Yates's Bar, Alcester Street (Yates)

RUGBY

Coombe Abbey ❯ Countryside Park, Visitor Centre (Coventry)

Rugby ❯ Benn Hall, Newbold Road (Hall hrs)

Caldecott Park (Daytime)
Ken Marriott Leisure Centre (Centre hrs)
Newbold Quarry
North Street Car Park
Rugby Art Gallery, Museum & Library (2)
(Building hrs)
Visitors' Centre, Art Gallery & Museum (Centre hrs)
Churchside Arcade (Private)
Clock Towers Shopping Centre (2) (Private)
Frobisher Road Pavilion (Private)
Rugby Station, Platform 2 (Virgin)
Rupert Brooke, Castle Street (JDW)
Walkabout, High Street (Private)
Gala Bingo, North Street (Gala)

SANDWELL

Cradley Heath ❯ Lower High Street, Car Park (9.00-17.30)
Bus Station, Forge Lane (Centro)
Moon Under Water, High Street (JDW)

Great Barr ❯ Scott Arms Shopping Centre
Gala Bingo, Walsall Road (Gala)

Oldbury ❯ Sandwell & Dudley Station, Bromford Road

Rowley Regis ❯ Henderson Way, Car Park
The Britannia, Halesowen Street (JDW)

Smethwick ❯ Stoney Lane, Car Park (9.00-17.30)
Bearwood Bus Station, Adkins Lane (Centro)
Smethwick Galton Bridge Station
(London Midland)
Sampson Lloyd, Cape Hill (JDW)

Wednesbury ❯ The Shambles
Bus Station, Holyhead Road (Centro)
The Bellwether, Walsall Street (JDW)
Gala Bingo, St James Bridge (Gala)

West Bromwich ❯ Sandwell Valley Country Park (7)
Bus Station, Ring Road (6.00-24.00) (Centro)
The Hawthorns Station (London Midland)
Sandwell Centre, Kings Square (Private)
Sandwell Centre, Queens Square (Private)
Billiard Hall, St Michael's Ringway (JDW)

SHROPSHIRE

Albrighton ❯ Crown Car Park

Bishops Castle ❯ Station Street Car Park

Bridgnorth ❯ Fox Corner, St John's Street
Innage Lane Car Park
Listley Street Car Park
Castle Grounds (Park hrs) (Town Council)
Sainsbury's Store, Whitburn Street (Sainsburys)
Jewel of the Severn, High Street (JDW)

Broseley ❯ Dark Lane Car Park

Church Stretton ❯ Easthope Road Car Park
Carding Mill Valley (National Trust)

Clee Hill ❯ High Street, A4117

Clun ❯ Newcastle Road Car Park

Craven Arms ❯ Shrewsbury Road

Ellesmere ❯ Cross Street
The Moors

Ford ❯ A458 Lay-by

Highley ❯ High Street Car Park

Ludlow ❯ Castle Street Car Park
Smithfield Car Park
Ludlow Station (Arriva Wales)
British Legion Club, Mill Street (RBL)

Market Drayton ❯ Towers Lawn
Hippodrome, Queen Street (JDW)

Much Wenlock ❯ St Mary's Lane Car Park

Oswestry ❯ Beatrice Street Car Park
Central Car Park, English Walls
Cae Glass Park (Town Council)
Wilfred Owen, Willow Street (JDW)

Pontesbury ❯ School Bank

Prees Heath ❯ Car & Lorry Park

Shifnal ❯ Aston Street Place

Shrewsbury ❯ Raven Meadow Bus Station (8.00-23.00)
Abbey Foregate (8.00-17.00) (Town Council)
Hills Lane (8.00-17.00) (Town Council)
Quarry Bottom (Daytime) (Town Council)
Quarry Top (Daytime) (Town Council)
Sydney Avenue (8.00-16.30) (Town Council)
Shrewsbury Station (Arriva Wales)
Shrewsbury Hotel, Bridge Place (JDW)
Yates's Bar, The Mardol (Yates)
Gala Bingo, Castle Gate (Gala)

Snailbeach ❯ Village Hall

Wem ❯ High Street Car Park

Whitchurch ❯ Brownlow Street
White Lion Meadow

SOLIHULL

Berkswell ❯ Bear Inn, Spencer Lane (Private)

Castle Bromwich ❯ The Farthings, Green Lane (Private)

Chelmsley Wood ❯ Chelmsley Wood Library (Library hrs)

Dorridge ❯ Dorridge Station (London Midland)
Drum & Monkey, Four Ashes Road (Private)

Marston Green ❯ Marston Green Station (London Midland)
Marston Green Tavern, Station Road (Private)

NEC ❯ Birmingham International Station (Virgin)
Little Owl, Bickenhill Parkway (M&B)

Olton ❯ Olton Station (London Midland)

Sheldon ❯ Rileys, Hobs Moat Road (Private)

West Midlands

Shirley		Colebrook Inn, Haslucks Green Rd (M&B) The Drawbridge, Drawbridge Road (Private) Plume of Feathers, Stratford Road (Private) Sharmans Cross, Prospect Lane (Private)
Solihull	❯	Mell Square Solihull Arts Complex (Centre hrs) Solihull Central Library (Library hrs) Touchwood Shopping Centre (Private) Solihull Station (London Midland) Apres Bar, Poplar Road (Private) Assembley Rooms, Poplar Road (JDW) Boat Inn, Catherine de Barnes (Private) Coach House, Herbert Road (Marstons) Druckers Café, Touchwood Centre (Private) Greville Arms, Damson Lane (M&B) Jimmy Spices, Station Road (Private) Nandos, Mill Lane Arcade (Nandos) Nog, Station Road (Private) O'Neils, Poplar Road (Private) Saddlers Arms, Warwick Road (Private) Slug & Lettuce, Touchwood Centre (Private) Town House, Warwick Road (Private) White Swan, Station Road (JDW) Yates's Bar, Station Road (Yates)
Widney Manor	❯	Widney Manor Station (London Midland)

SOUTH STAFFORDSHIRE

Essington M6	❯	Hilton Park Services, J10a/11 M6 (Moto)
Himley	❯	Himley House (Private)

STAFFORD

Little Haywood	❯	Jubilee Playing Fields (Parish Council)
Milford	❯	Brocton Lane (M&F)
Stafford	❯	Bridge Street MSCP, opp Civic Centre Broad Street Car Park, by Shopmobility Civic Centre, Ground Floor (Office hrs) Doxey Road Lorry Park North Walls Car Park

Rowley Park Sports Stadium (Park hrs)
Stafford Castle Visitor Centre, Newport Road
Stafford Crematorium (8.00-dusk)
Stafford Market (M&F) (Market hrs)
Victoria Park (Park hrs)
Stafford Station, Platform 1 (Virgin)
Picture House, Bridge Street (JDW)
Yates's Bar, Gaolgate Street (Yates)
Gala Bingo, Silkmore Lane (Gala)

Stone ❯ Crown Street Car Park
Station Road
Post of Stone, Granville Square (JDW)

Stone M6 ❯ Stafford North Services, J14/15 M6 (Moto)

STAFFORDSHIRE MOORLANDS

Alstonfield ❯ Car Park (Peak District NP)

Biddulph ❯ Biddulph Grange Country Park
Town Hall
Wharf Road Car Park
Greenway Bank Country Park (Staffs CC)
Bradley Green, High Street (JDW)

Blythe Bridge ❯ Cheadle Road

Cheadle ❯ Tape Street Car Park

Cheddleton ❯ Deep Hayes Country Park (Staffs CC)

Cotton ❯ The Star Caravan & Camping Park (Private)

Hulme End ❯ Visitor Centre (Centre hrs)

Ilam ❯ Wetton Mill, Ilam Park (National Trust)

Leek ❯ Bus Station, Smithfield Centre
Silk Street Car Park (7.00-18.00)
Blackshaw Moor Caravan Club Site
(Caravan Club)

Mildale ❯ Mildale Village

Oakamoor	❯	Oakamoor Picnic Areas (Staffs CC)
Rudyard	❯	Lakeside (Visitor Centre hrs)
Waterhouses	❯	Car Park (Peak District NP)
Wetley Rocks	❯	Consall Nature Park (Staffs CC)
Wetton	❯	Wetton Village

STOKE-ON-TRENT

Abbey Hulton ❯ Abbey Hulton Local Centre, Abbots Rd (Office hrs)

Blurton ❯ Blurton Local Centre, Finstock Ave (Office hrs)
Gables, Trentham Road (Marstons)

Chell Heath ❯ Chell Heath Local Centre, Cornhill Rd (Office hrs)

Etruria ❯ Odeon Cinema, Festival Park (Odeon)
Tenpin, Marina Way (Private)

Fenton ❯ City Road Car Park
KFC, King Street (KFC)
Gala Bingo, Victoria Road (Gala)

Hanley ❯ Crown Bank, Stafford Street
Debenhams Store, Potteries Centre (Debenhams)
Caffe Nero, Parliament Road (Private)
Reginald Mitchell, Parliament Row (JDW)
Varsity, Percy Street (Barracuda)
Walkabout, Trinity Street (Private)
Dudson Museum, Hope Street (Private)
Gala Bingo, Albion Square (Gala)
Grosvenor Casino, New Centuary Sq (Private)

Longton ❯ Longton Local Centre, Commerce St (Office hrs)
Longton Market, Transport St. (Market hrs)

Meir ❯ Meir Local Centre, Uttoxeter Rd (Office hrs)
Weston Road car park

Norton ❯ Norton Local Centre, St Nicholas Ave (Office hrs)

Smallthorne	❯	Community Drive
Stoke	❯	Kingsway car park South Wolfe Street Stoke-on-Trent Station (Virgin) The Wheatsheaf, Church Street (JDW) Michelin Athletics Club, Trent Vale (Private)
Tunstall	❯	Butterfield Place (2)
Weston Coyney	❯	Park Hall Country Park (2)

STRATFORD ON AVON

Alcester	❯	Bulls Head Yard, Car Park Royal Oak, High Street (Private)
Bidford-on-Avon	❯	High Street Big Meadow (Parish Council)
Earlswood	❯	Reservoir, The Common (Private)
Henley-in-Arden	❯	Station Road
Shipston-on-Stour	❯	Telegraph Street
Southam	❯	Wood Street
Stratford-upon-Avon	❯	Avonbank Gardens, Old Town Bridgefoot, Car Park Recreation Ground, Play Area Waterside (M&F) Windsor Street, Car Park Town Square Shopping Centre (Private) Visitor & Leisure Centre, Bridgeway (Private) Ripple Café, Swans Nest Lane (Private) Golden Bee, Sheep Street (JDW) Yates's Bar, Windsor Street (Yates)
Studley	❯	Birmingham Road
Warmington	❯	Wobbly Wheel, Warwick Road (Private)

TAMWORTH

Tamworth ❯ Aldergate (8.00-6.00)
Castle Pleasure Grounds (Park hrs)
Wiggington Road Cemetery (Cemetery hrs)
Ankerside Shopping Centre (Private)
Co-op Store, Colehill (Private)
The Bolebridge, Bolebridge Street (JDW)
Silk Kite, Church Street (JDW)
Yates's Bar, Lower Gungate (Yates)

Tamworth, M42 ❯ Tamworth Services, J10 M42/A5 (Moto)

TELFORD & WREKIN

Brookside ❯ Brookside Community Centre

Dawley ❯ King Street (Parish Council)

Hadley ❯ District Centre (Parish Council)

Ironbridge ❯ The Square
The Wharfage

Madeley ❯ High Street (Parish Council)

Malinslee ❯ Town Park (Parish Council)

Newport ❯ Stafford Street Car Park (Town Council)

Oakengates ❯ Stafford Road (Parish Council)

Sutton Hill ❯ Sutton Hill Community Centre

Telford ❯ Telford Shopmobility, Red Oak Car Park (Private)
Telford Shopping Centre (3) (Private)
Debenhams Store, Sherwood Sq (Debenhams)
Telford Centre Bus Station (Private)
Telford Central Station (London Midland)
Thomas Botfield, Telford Shopping Centre (JDW)

Wellington ❯ The Parade (Town Council)
Walker Street (Town Council)

WALSALL

Aldridge ❯ Anchor Road, Shopping Precinct
Gala Bingo, Anchor Road (Gala)

Bloxwich ❯ High Street/Wolverhampton Road
Asda, High Street

Pelsall ❯ Norton Road

Walsall ❯ St Pauls Bus Station (7.00-21.00) (Centro)
Walsall Station (London Midland)
The Imperial, Darwall Street (JDW)
Park Tavern, Broadway North (Private)
Varsity, Darwall Street (Barracuda)
Yates's Bar, Leicester Street (Yates)
Gala Bingo, Jerome Retail Park (Gala)

Willenhall ❯ Market Car Park
The Malthouse, New Road (JDW)

WARWICK

Kenilworth ❯ Abbey End (Daytime)
Abbey Fields (Daytime)

Leamington Spa ❯ Brunswick Street (Daytime)
Covent Gardens MSCP (Daytime)
Crown Way (Daytime)
Jephson Gardens (Daytime)
Leamington Cemetery (Daytime)
Regent Grove (Daytime)
St Peter's Car Park (Daytime)
Victoria Park (Daytime)
Leamington Spa Station, Platform 2 (Chiltern Rlwy)
Benjamin Satchwell, The Parade (JDW)
Yates's Bar, Warwick Street (Yates)
Warwick Racecourse Caravan Club Site
(Caravan Club)

Radford Semele ❯ White Lion, Southam Road (Private)

Warwick ❯ Market Place (Daytime)
Myton Fields (Summer and weekends, daytime)
Pageant Gardens (Daytime)
St Nicholas Park (Daytime)

Shire Hall (Warwicks CC) (CP)
Thomas Lloyd, Market Place (JDW)

WOLVERHAMPTON

Bilston ❯ Market (7.00-21.00)
Bus Station, Coach Lounge (Centro)
Bilston Craft Gallery (Private)
Sir Henry Newbold, High Street (JDW)

Compton ❯ Odd Fellows, Compton Road (Marstons)

Merry Hill ❯ Merry Hill, Trysull Road (Private)

Tettenhall ❯ Stockwell Road (7.00-21.00)

Wednesfield ❯ High Street (7.00-21.00)
Royal Tiger, High Street (JDW)
AMF Bowl Bentley Bridge (AMF)

Wolverhampton ❯ Art Gallery, Lichfield Street (Gallery hrs)
Ashmore Park, Griffiths Drive (7.00-18.00)
Civic Centre, St Peters Square
Faulkland Street Coach Station (7.00-19.00)
WCityStop, Mander Centre (Office hrs)
Wolverhampton Market, School Street
West Park (Park hrs)
Bus Station, Pipers Row (Centro)
Mander Shopping Centre (Private)
Wulfrun Shopping Centre (2) (Private)
Beatties Store, Victoria Street (Private)
Littlewoods Store, Bilston Street (Private)
Wolverhampton Station, Platform 1 (Virgin)
Bantock House Café, Finchfield Rd (Private)
Edwards, North Street (M&B)
Goose in the City, Lichfield Street (M&B)
Hog's Head, Stafford Street (Private)
Moon Under Water, Lichfield Street (JDW)
Nandos, 23 Queen Street (Nandos)
Oceana, Bilston Street (Private)
O'Neills, Lichfield Street (M&B)
Revolution, Princess Street (Private)
Rothwells, Lichfield Street (Private)
Scream, Wulfruna Street (Private)
The Tube, Princes Street (Private)
Varsity, Stafford Street (Barracuda)

Walkabout, Queen Street (Private)
Yates's Bar, Queens Square (Yates)
Express Bowling, Birmingham Road (AMF)
Gala Bingo, Bushbury Lane (Gala)
Molineux Stadium (Wolves FC)

WORCESTER

Worcester ❯ Barbourne Lane (7.45-18.20)
Bull Ring, St Johns (7.45-18.20)
Reindeer Court Shopping Centre (Private)
The Crown, Crown Passage (JDW)
Nandos, 55 Friar Street (Nandos)
Postal Order, Foregate Street (JDW)
Gala Bingo, Foregate Street (Gala)

WYCHAVON

Broadway ❯ Church Close Car Park
Milestone Ground Car Park
Shear House Car Park
Broadway Caravan Club Site (Caravan Club)

Droitwich ❯ Lido Park (8.00-18.00)
St Andrews Square
Droitwich Spa Station (London Midland)

Evesham ❯ Abbey Park (Daytime)
Oat Street (8.00-21.00)
Old Brewery Car Park (9.00-18.00)
Viaduct Meadow (Daytime)
Waterside
Evesham Station (Gt Western)
Old Swanne Inn, High Street (JDW)

Pershore ❯ Church Walk (8.00-18.00)
High Street Car Park (8.00-21.00)

WYRE FOREST

Bewdley ❯ Car Park, off Load Street
Dog Lane Car Park
George Hotel, Load Street (JDW)
Running Horse Inn, Long Bank (Private)

West Midlands

Kidderminster ❯ Brintons Park, Sutton Road
Broadwaters Park, Stourbridge Road
Market Street (Daytime)
Rowlands Hill Shopping Centre (7.00-17.30)
Swan Shopping Centre (Private)
Wyre Forest Glades Arena (Private)
Kidderminster Station (London Midland)
The Penny Black, Bull Ring (JDW)
Watermill, Park Lane (Private)
Connect, Blackwell Street (Worcs CC) (CP)

Stourport-on-Severn ❯ Raven Street Car Park
Severn Meadows Car Park, by Civic Centre
Vale Road Car Park
Ye Olde Crown, Bridge Street (JDW)

NORTH WEST ENGLAND

ALLERDALE

Allonby ❯ Central Green, by Play Area
West Green

Aspatria ❯ Queen Street Car Park

Buttermere ❯ Village Car Park (Lake District NP)

Cockermouth ❯ Harris Park
Main Street

Keswick ❯ Belle Close Car Park
Central Car Park
Lakeside Car Park, behind Theatre
Station Platform

Maryport ❯ Harbour, Irish Street
High Street
Promenade

Rosthwaite ❯ By Car Park (Lake District NP)

Silloth ❯ The Green
Skinburness, opp. Solway Village

Wigton ❯ Market Hall

Workington ❯ Harrington Marina
Town Centre
Henry Bessemer, New Oxford Street (JDW)

BARROW-IN-FURNESS

Barrow-in-Furness ❯ Amphitheatre, Manor Road
Barrow Park, Bowling Pavilion (Park hrs)
Fell Street, Car Park
Roa Island
Debenhams Store, Portland Wk (Debenhams)
The Furness Railway", Abbey Road (JDW)
Yates's Bar, Duke Street (Yates)

Dalton-in-Furness ❯ Tudor Square

Walney Island	❯	Earnse Bay, West Shore Road

BLACKBURN WITH DARWEN

Blackburn	❯	Market Way
		Witton Country Park, Preston Old Road
		The Mall Blackburn (2) (Private)
		Debenhams Store, Northgate (Debenhams)
		Blackburn Station (Northern Rail)
		Boddington Arms, Myerscough Road (Private)
		The Postal Order, Darwen Street (JDW)
		BowlPlex, Peel Leisure Park (BowlPlex)
		Gala Bingo, Ainsworth Street (Gala)

Darwen	❯	Town Hall, Parliament Street

Roddlesworth	❯	Ryal Fold Information Centre (Utd Utilities)

BLACKPOOL

Blackpool - Central	❯	Bethesda Square, Central Drive
		Blackpool Council Offices (Office hrs)
		Carleton Cremetorium
		Central Car Park, Central Drive/New Bonny Rd
		Layton Square, Westcliffe Drive
		Lonsdale Coach Park
		Lytham Road/Station Road
		Solaris Centre (CP)
		Talbot Road Bus Station
		Town Hall, Talbot Square (Office hrs)
		Victoria Street, Town Centre
		Centre for Independent Living [Planned] (CP)
		Magistrates Court (Court Service)
		Festival Shopping Mall (Private)
		Blackpool North Station (Northern Rail)
		Blackpool Pleasure Beach (3) (Private)
		Blackpool Tower (Private)
		Central Pier, Family Bar (Private)
		North Pier (Private)
		South Pier Amusements (Private)
		Winter Gardens (Private)
		The Auctioneer, Lytham Road (JDW)
		Belle Vue, Whitegate Drive (Private)
		Brannigans, Market Street (Private)
		King Edward VII Hotel, Central Drive (Private)

Litten Tree, Queen Street (Private)
Outside Inn, Whitehills Industrial Pk (Private)
Swift Hound, Festival Park (Private)
Walkabout, Queen Street (Private)
Yates's Bar, 407-411 The Promenade (Yates)

Blackpool - North ❯

Bispham Tram Station, Queens Promenade
Bispham Village Car Park
Cocker Square/Promenade
Gynn Square, Promenade
Little Bispham, Queens Prom/Princes Way
Uncle Tom's Cabin, Queens Promenade
The Highlands, 206 Queens Promenade (Private)
Red Lion, Devonshire Sq., Bispham (Private)

Blackpool – South ❯

Central Gateway
Harrowside, Promenade South
Highfield Road, by Library
Starr Gate Tram Loop

Marton ❯

Clifton Arms, Preston New Road (Private)

Blackpool Council
BUILDING A BETTER COMMUNITY FOR ALL

New fully modernised facilities are available throughout Blackpool. All
providing a 24 hour service. Each location is accessible with a RADAR
key and has baby changing facilities

Our toilets can be found at:

Little Bispham (p)
Cabin (p)
Bispham Village (p)
Layton Square (p)
Gynn Square (p)
Cocker Square
Central Car Park
Seasiders Way

Victoria Street
Bethesda Square
Lonsdale Coach Park
Lytham Road
Highfield Road
Harrowside
Starr Gate (p)
Bispham Tram Station (p)

(p) = Located on the Promenade
All locations have facilities for the disabled
Visit our website www.blackpool.gov.uk and view the location map

Blackpool South Caravan Club Site
(Caravan Club)

BOLTON

Bolton ❯ Back Cheapside
Moor Lane Bus Station
Old Hall Street (Mon-Sat, 8.30-17.30)
Compton Place, Car Park (Private)
Bolton Station, nr Footbridge (Northern Rail)
Jumbles Country Park (Utd Utilities)
Nandos, Middlebrook Retail Park (Nandos)
Spinning Mule, Nelson Square (JDW)
Varsity, Churchgate (Barracuda)
Yates's Bar, Bradshawgate (Yates)

Farnworth ❯ Farnworth Bus Station [Closed at present]
Moses Gate Country Park

Horwich ❯ Captain Street
Horwich Parkway Station (Northern Rail)

Westhoughton ❯ Market Street
Robert Shaw, Market Street (JDW)

BURNLEY

Burnley ❯ Briarcliffe Road, by Hospital
Burnley Bus Station (5.00-23.30)

Cemetery Chapel, Rossendale Road
(Chapel hrs)
Market Hall (Trading hrs)
Millennium Car Park, Brick Street (8.00-18.00)
Queens Park
Scott Park (Park hrs)
Thompson Park, Ormerod Road (Park hrs)
Yorkshire Street
Burnley Central Station (Northern Rail)
Brun Lea, Manchester Road (JDW)
Walkabout, Hammerton Street (Private)
Gala Bingo Club, Centenary Way (Gala)

Padiham ❯ Church Street

BURY

Bury ❯ Bus Interchange
Kay Gardens
Mill Gate Shopping Centre (Private)
Art Picture House, Haymarket Street (JDW)
Robert Peel, Market Place (JDW)
Yates's Bar, Market Street (Yates)
Burrs Country Park Caravan Club Site
(Caravan Club)

Prestwich ❯ Longfield Precinct

Radcliffe ❯ Market Hall

Ramsbottom ❯ Market Chambers

Tottington ❯ Market Street

CARLISLE

Brampton ❯ Car Park, High Cross Street
Milburn Court (Daytime)
Talkin Tarn (Park hrs)

Carlisle ❯ Bitts Park (Park hrs)
Cathedral Grounds
Covered Market (Trading hrs)
Old Town Hall, English Street (Daytime)
St Nicholas, Botchergate (Daytime)

Town Dyke Orchard Car Park (Daytime)
Upperby Park (Daytime)
Debenhams Store. The Lanes (Debenhams)
The Lanes Shopping Centre (Private)
Carlisle Station, Platforms 1 & 4 (Virgin)
Bar Code, Botchergate (Private)
Bar Suede, The Cresent (Private)
Casa, Botchergate (Private)
Club XS, West Walls (Private)
Gosling Bridge Inn, Kingstown Road (Private)
The Griffin, Court Square (Private)
The Holme, Denton Street (Private)
Jumpin Jaks, English Gate Plaza (Private)
Leonardo's, Lonsdale Street (Private)
Litten Tree, Botchergate (Private)
Lloyds Bar, Botchergate (JDW)
Mood, Botchergate (Private)
Teza, English Gate Plaza (Private)
Turf Tavern, Newmarket Road, The Sands (Private)
Walkabout, English Gate Plaza (Private)
William Rufus, Botchergate (JDW)
Woodrow Wilson, Botchergate (JDW)
Yates's Bar, English Street (Yates)
Carlisle Bowl, Currock Road (AMF)
Gala Bingo Club, Englishgate Plaza (Gala)

Dalston ➤ The Square (Daytime)

Longtown ➤ Bank Street (Daytime)

Penton ➤ Nicolforest Public Hall (external access)

Southwaite M6 ➤ Southwaite Services, J41/42 M6 (Moto)

Stapleton ➤ Stapleton Public Hall (external access)

CHESHIRE EAST

Alderley Edge ➤ West Street
The Wizard Car Park (National Trust)
De Trafford, Congleton Road (Private)

Alsager ➤ Crewe Road

Audlem ➤ Cheshire Street Car Park

Bollington ❯ Aldington Road (9.00-16.30)
Poll Bank Car Park

Brereton Heath ❯ Country Park

Congleton ❯ Bridestones Shopping Centre
Congleton Park
Market Street
West Heath Shopping Centre
The Counting House, Swan Bank (JDW)

Crewe ❯ Bus Station, Delamere Street
Pedley Street
Queens Park, Victoria Avenue (Park hrs)
Crewe Station, Platforms 5 and 6-11 (Virgin)
The Earl, Nantwich Road (Private)
Gaffers Row, Victoria Street (JDW)

Disley ❯ Station Approach

Handforth ❯ Church Road
Millers, Wilmslow Road (Private)

Knutsford ❯ King Street Car Park
Northwich Road
Stanley Road, by Supermarket

Knutsford M6 ❯ Knutsford Services, J18/19 M6 (Moto)

Langley ❯ Trentabank Car Park (Peak Dist NP)

Lower Peover ❯ Bells of Peover The Cobbles (Private)

Macclesfield ❯ Churchill Way (8.15-17.15)
Park Green
Riverside Park, off Beech Lane (8.45-16.15)
Society Rooms, Park Green (JDW)
Macclesfield Bowl, Lyme Green Bus. Park (AMF)

Mere ❯ Kilton Inn, Hoo Green (Private)

Middlewich ❯ France Hayhurst Pavilion (Park hrs)
Southway, off Wheelock Street
Town Bridge, Leadsmithy Street

Nantwich ❯ Civic Hall Car Park, Beam Street

Nantwich Market (CP)
Snowhill Car Park, Wall Lane

Poynton ❯ Fountain Place
Nelson Pit Visitor Centre (Centre hrs)

Prestbury ❯ Bridge Green

Sandbach ❯ High Street, by Town Hall

Timbersbrook ❯ Picnic Site
Pool Bank Car Park

Wilmslow ❯ South Drive
Twinnies Bridge Country Park (Weekend, daytime)
Bollin Fee, Swan Street (JDW)

CHESHIRE WEST & CHESTER

Alvanley ❯ White Lion Inn, Manley Road (Private)

Barnton ❯ Lydyett Lane (Daytime)

Cheshire Oaks ❯ McArthur Glen Designer Outlet (Private)
Nandos, Stanney Lane (Nandos)
Old Orleans, The Coliseum (Private)

Chester ❯ Foregate Street
Frodsham Street
The Groves, nr Suspension Bridge (8.00-20.00)
Little Roodee, Car/Coach Park (9.30-17.00)
Princess Street Bus Station
Princess Street, under Market (8.00-18.00)
Union Street, by Grosvenor Park (Easter-Sept)
Bus Station (Private)
The Mall Grosvenor (Private)
Chester Station, Concourse (Arriva Wales)
Forest House, Love Street (JDW)
Square Bottle, Foregate Street (JDW)
Yates's Bar, Frodsham Street (Yates)

Cuddington ❯ Norley Road (Daytime)

Dunham Hill ❯ Wheatsheaf, Dunham Hill (Private)

Ellesmere Port  Council Offices, Civic Way (Office hrs)
Market (Market hrs)
Town Centre (M&F) (Daytime)
Grace Arms, Stanney Lane (Private)
Thomas Telford, Whitby Road (JDW)
Wheatsheaf, Overpool Road (JDW)

Frodsham Moors Lane (Daytime)

Little Stanney Chester Fairoaks Caravan Club Site
(Caravan Club)

Neston Brook Street

Northwich Applemarket Street (Daytime)
Leicester Street (Daytime)
Penny Black, Witton Street (JDW)

Parkgate Moston Square, School Lane

Tarporley High Street (Daytime)

Upton	❯	Chester Zoo, The Ark Restaurant (Private)
Weaverham	❯	Church Road (Daytime)
Winsford	❯	Fountain Court [Closed at present] Queens Arms, Dene Drive (JDW)

CHORLEY

Adlington	❯	Babylon Lane
Chorley	❯	Astley Park, Coach House Market Place, Cleveland Street Pall Mall Millers, Bolton Road (Private) Sir Henry Tate, New Market Street (JDW) Gala Bingo Club, Market Street (Gala)
Rivington	❯	Great House Inf. Centre (Utd Utilities) Rivington Lane Car Park (Utd Utilities)
Whittle-le-Woods	❯	Malthouse Farm, Moss Lane (Private)

COPELAND

Bootle	❯	Village Car Park (Parish Council)
Cleator Moor	❯	Market Place Car Park
Egremont	❯	Chapel Street
Eskdale	❯	The Green Station (R&E Rlwy) Ireton Road Station (R&E Rlwy)
Gosforth	❯	Car Park (Parish Council)
Haverigg	❯	Foreshore (Town Council)
Millom	❯	The Park, St Georges Road Lancashire Road (Town Council)
Seascale	❯	Foreshore, by Car Park
St Bees Beach	❯	Foreshore Car Park

Whitehaven	❯	James Street
		Whitehaven Station (Northern Rail)
		Bransty Arch, Bransty Row (JDW)

EDEN

Alston	❯	Town Hall
		Station Car Park (S Tynedale Rlwy)
Appleby	❯	Broad Close Car Park
		Tourist Information Centre, Moot Hall
Brough		Main Street
Dufton	❯	Car Park
Garrigill	❯	Village Hall (Hall Committee)
Glenridding	❯	Jenkins Field Car Park
		Ullswater Information Centre (Lake District NP)
Kirkby Stephen	❯	Stoneshot Car Park
Patterdale	❯	opp. White Lion
Penrith	❯	Bluebell Lane, Little Dockray
		Castle Park
		Sandgate Bus Station/Car Park
		Southend Road Car Park
		Penrith Station, Platform 1 (Virgin)
Pooley Bridge	❯	by Tourist Information Centre
Threkeld	❯	behind Village Hall
Troutbeck	❯	Troutbeck Head Caravan Club Site
		(Caravan Club)

FYLDE

Freckleton	❯	Freckleton Centre
Greenhalgh	❯	Fairfield Arms, Fleetwood Road (Private)
Kirkham	❯	Church Street
		Kirkham & Wesham Station (Northern Rail)

Lytham ❯ East Beach
Lowther Pavilion, West Beach
Pleasant Street Car Park
Stanner Bank, Fairhaven Lake

St Anne's ❯ Fairhaven Road
Promenade Gardens, by Monument
St Annes Road West, by Station
Trawl Boat Inn, Wood Street (JDW)

HALTON

Daresbury ❯ Ring O'Bells, Chester Road (Private)

Runcorn ❯ Runcorn Station, Platform 1 (Virgin)
Ferry Boat, Church Street (JDW)
Widnes The Premier, Albert Road (JDW)

HYNDBURN

Accrington ❯ Peel Street Bus Station
Arndale Shopping Centre (Private)

Clayton-le-Moors ❯ Public Library

Great Harwood ❯ Blackburn Road, Town Centre

KNOWSLEY

Huyton ❯ Bus Station (Merseytravel)

Kirkby ❯ Cherryfield Drive Bus Station
Kirkby Market
Gold Balance, New Town Gardens (JDW)
Gala Bingo, Telegraph Way (Gala)

Prescot ❯ Grapes Hotel, St Helens Road (Private)

LANCASTER

Bolton-le-Sands ❯ Community Centre (Private)

Carnforth ❯ Market Square (Private)

Carnforth M6   ❯   Burton-in-Kendal Services, M6 J35/35 (Moto)

Caton   ❯   Bull Beck Picnic Area
Crook of Lune Car Park (Lancs CC)

Glasson Dock   ❯   Condor Green Picnic Area (Lancs CC)

Heysham   ❯   Strawberry Gardens, Heysham Road (Private)

Lancaster   ❯   Bulk Street Car Park
Bus Station
Market Gate
Market Hall
Mitre House, China Street
Nelson Street Car Park
St Nickolas Arcade
Williamson Park
Lancaster Station Platforms 3 & 4 (Virgin)
Alexander Square (Lancaster University)
Green Ayre, North Road (JDW)
Sir Richard Owen, Spring Garden St (JDW)
Varsity, George Street (Barracuda)
Walkabout, Dalton Square (Private)
Yates's Bar, Dalton Square (Yates)
Gala Bingo Club, King Street (Gala)

Lancaster M6   ❯   Lancaster Services, J32/33 M6 (Moto)

Middleton   ❯   Parish Hall (Private)

Morecambe		Central Promenade, by Bubbles Pool (2) Central Promenade, Clock Tower Festival Market Hall Happy Mount Car Park Library Car Park, by Arndale Centre Morecambe Leisure Park (Summer) Stone Jetty West End Promenade Eric Bartholomew, Euston Road (JDW) Gala Bingo Club, Marine Road East (Gala)
Silverdale		Gaskell Hall (Private)

LIVERPOOL

Allerton		Yates's Bar, Allerton Road (Yates)
Clark Gardens		Allerton Hall, Springwood Avenue (Private)
Croxteth		Gala Bingo, Stonedale Retail Park (Gala)

Hunts Cross ❯ Hunts Cross Station, Platform 3 (MerseyRail)

Garston ❯ Garston Library (Library hrs)

Gateacre ❯ Bear & Staff, Gateacre Brow (Private)

Liverpool City Centre ❯ Central Library, William Brown St (Library hrs)
Albert Dock, The Colonnades (2) (Private)
Clayton Square Shopping Centre (Private)
Liverpool One, Wall Street (Private) (CP)
St Johns Shopping Centre (Private)
Coach Station, Norton St (Nat Express)
Queen Square Bus Station (Merseytravel)
Lime Street Station, Concourse (Network Rail)
Liverpool Central Station (MerseyRail)
Haigh Building, Maryland Street (LJM University)
Royal Liverpool Hospital (Hospital)
Fall Well, St John's Way (JDW)
Fly in the Loaf, Hardman Street (Private)
Ha! Ha! Bar, Albert Dock (Private)
Knotty Ash Hotel, East Prescot Rd (Private)
Lime Kiln, Fleet Street (JDW)
Nandos, Liverpool One (Nandos)
Nandos, 6 Queen Square (Nandos)
Norwegian Blue, Bold Street (Private)
The Picturedrome, 286 Kensington (JDW)
Rat & Parrot, Queen Square (Private)
The Raven, Walton Vale (JDW)
Richard John Blackler, Charlotte Row (JDW)
Thomas Frost, Walton Road (JDW)
Walkabout, Fleet Street (Private)
The Welkin, Whitechapel (JDW)
Yates's Bar, Queens Square (Yates)

Norris Green ❯ Lifestyles Ellergate (Centre hrs)

Speke ❯ Pizza Hut, New Mersey Retail Park (Private)
The Argosy, John Lennon Airport (JDW)

Stoneycroft ❯ The Navigator, Queens Drive (JDW)

Toxteth ❯ Lifestyles Toxteth (Centre hrs)

Walton ❯ Lifestyles Alsop (Centre hrs)

Wavertree ❯ Wavertree Technology Park Station (Northern Rail)

Gala Bingo, Wavertree Road (Gala)

MANCHESTER

Belle Vue ❯❯ Gala Bingo, Hyde Road (Gala)

Cheetham Hill ❯❯ Humphrey Street

Chorlton-cum-Hardy ❯❯ Bus Terminus, Barlow Moor Road
Manchester Road
Sedge Lynn, Manchester Road (JDW)

Didsbury ❯❯ Barlow Moor Road, by Library
Nandos, Parrs Wood Leisure (Nandos)

Fallowfield ❯❯ Great Central, Wilmslow Road (JDW)
Nandos, 351 Wimslow Road (Nandos)

Harpurhey ❯❯ Gala Bingo, North City Shopping Centre (Gala)

Heaton Park ❯❯ Sainsbury's Store, Heaton Park Rd West
(Sainsbury)

Levenshulme ❯❯ Albert Road, off Stockport Road

Manchester Airport ❯❯ Bus Station (GMPTE)
Manchester Airport Station (Transpennine)

North West England

Manchester City Centre ❯
Castlefield, off Liverpool Street
Church Street/Tib Street
John Dalton Street/Deansgate
Parker Street, Piccadilly Bus Station
Stevenson Square
Town Hall Extension, Mount Street (Daytime)
Arndale Centre (Private)
Shudehill Interchange (GMPTE)
Deansgate Station (Northern Rail)
Piccadilly Station (2) (Network Rail)
Victoria Station (Northern Rail)
Debenhams Store, Market St (Debenhams)
Ha! Ha! Bar, Spinningfields (Private)
Manchester & County, Piccadilly (JDW)
Moon Under Water, Deansgate (JDW)
Nandos, Arndale Centre (Nandos)
Nandos, Hardman St, Spinningfields (Nandos)
Nandos, Oxford Road (Nandos)
Nandos, The Printworks (Nandos)
Norwegian Blue, Corporation Street (Private)
Old Orleans, Withy Grove (Private)
The Paramount, Oxford Road (JDW)
Sawyers Arms, Deansgate (Private)
Seven Stars, Dantzic Street (JDW)
Varsity, Wimslow Park (Barracuda)
Walkabout, Quay Street (Private)
Waterhouse, Princess Street (JDW)
Yates's Bar, Portland Street (Yates)

Rusholme ❯
Ford Maddox Ford, Wilmslow Park (JDW)

Sportcity ❯
City of Manchester Stadium (Manchester City FC)

Withington ❯
Burton Road, by White Lion
Mill Lane, off Palatine Road

Wythenshawe ❯
Civic Centre
Hollyhedge Road, nr. Brownley Road
Wythenshawe Bus Station (GMPTE)
Gala Bingo, Rowlandsway (Gala)

OLDHAM

Chadderton ❯
Shopping Precinct (Daytime)

Greenfield ❯
Dovestones Reservoir

Greenfield Station (Northern Rail)

Oldham ⊗ Alexandra Park (Park hrs)
Civic Centre Bus Station (Daytime)
Tommyfield Market (Daytime)
Squire Knott, Yorkshire Street (JDW)
Up Steps Inn, High Street (JDW)
Walkabout, Yorkshire Street (Private)

Royton ⊗ Shopping Precinct (Daytime)

Uppermill ⊗ Uppermill Park (Daytime)

PENDLE

Barley ⊗ Picnic Area Car Park

Barnoldswick ⊗ Central Car Park, Fernlea Avenue
Letcliffe Park, Manchester Road

Barrowford ⊗ Gisburn Road/Church Road

Brierfield ⊗ Town Hall, Colne Road (8.00-18.00)

Colne ⊗ Bus Station, Craddock Road
Market Hall, Market Street (Market hrs)
Wallace Hartley, Church Street (JDW)

Cotton Tree ⊗ Ball Grove Picnic Area

Earby ⊗ Bus Station (8.00-18.00)
Colne Road, by Station Hotel (8.00-18.00)
Sough Park, Colne Road

Laneshawbridge ⊗ Keighley Road

Nelson ⊗ Bus Station, Broadway
Market Hall, Leeds Road (Market hrs)
Market Street

Newchurch ⊗ Village Centre

Salterforth ⊗ Kelbrook Lane/Earby Road

Wycoller ⊗ Wycoller Country Park (Lancs CC)

PRESTON

Preston ❯ Avenham MSCP (6.30-23.30
Avenham Park (Events only)
Bus Station (M&F) (Station hrs)
Guild Hall Concourse, 1st Floor (7.30-22.30)
Market Hall (Market hrs)
Moor Park Lodge, Garstang Road (Events only)
The Mall Preston (Private)
Preston Station, Platform 3 & Waiting Room (Virgin)
Centro Oriental Buffet, The Mall (Private)
The Greyfriar, Friargate (JDW)
Wall Street, Fishergate (Private)
Yates's Bar, Church Street (Yates)
Gala Bingo Club, Market Street (Gala)

Ribbleton ❯ Waverley/Ribbleton Park, Blackpool Road

RIBBLE VALLEY

Beacon Fell ❯ Bowland Visitor Centre (Lancs CC)

Bolton-by-Bowland ❯ Car Park

Chipping ❯ Car Park

Clitheroe ❯ Castle Field Grounds
Church Walk
Edisford, Riverside
Market
Waddington Road Cemetery
Clitheroe Station (Northern Rail)

Downham ❯ Car Park

Dunsop Bridge ❯ Car Park

Gisburn ❯ Auction Mart

Hurst Green ❯ St Paul's Club

Longridge ❯ King Street
Berry Lane

Mellor ❯ Mellor Lane

Ribchester	❯	Car Park
Sabden	❯	Car Park
Slaidburn	❯	Car Park
Whalley	❯	King Street Springwood Picnic Site (Lancs CC)

ROCHDALE

Greenfield	❯	Dunsmore Reservoir (Utd Utilities)
Heywood	❯	Bamford Road Edwin Waugh, Market Street (JDW)
Heywood M62	❯	Birch Services, J18/19 M62 (Moto)
Hollingworth Lake	❯	Lakebank (Daytime) Pavilion Café (Café hrs) Visitor Centre (Centre hrs) Millers, Hollingworth Lake (Private)
Littleborough	❯	The Square
Middleton	❯	Bus Station (GMPTE) Harbord Harbord, Long Street (JDW)
Ogden Reservoir	❯	Ogden Car Park (Utd Utilities)
Rochdale	❯	Bus Station Rochdale Exchange, Market Hall subway South Parade Wheatsheaf Centre (2) (Private) Regal Moon, The Butts (JDW) Yates's Bar, Yorkshire Street (Yates)
Whitworth	❯	Cowm Reservoir (Utd Utilities)

ROSSENDALE

Dunnockshaw	❯	Clowbridge Reservoir (Utd Utilities)
Haslingden Grane	❯	Clough Head Inf. Centre (Utd Utilities)

| Rawtenstall | ❯ | The Market, Newchurch Road
Old Cobblers Inn, New Hall Hey Rd (Private) |

ST HELENS

Bold Heath	❯	Griffin Inn, Warrington Road (Private)
Eccleston	❯	Royal Oak, East Lancashire Road (Private)
Garswood	❯	Garswood Station (Northern Rail)
Rainford	❯	Bottle & Glass Inn, St Helens Road (Private)
St Helens	❯	Brook Street (M&F) (Mon-Sat 9.00-18.00) Bus Station, Bickerstaffe Street (Merseytravel) St Mary's Arcade (Private) Carr Mill, East Lancashire Road (Private) Glass House, Market Street (JDW) Sefton Arms, Baldwin Street (Private)

SALFORD

Eccles	❯	Albert Street MSCP [Under review] Eccles Gateway Centre (Centre hrs) Eccles Metrolink/Bus Interchange (GMPTE) Albert Edward, Church Street (Private) Blue Bell, Monton Green (Private) Eccles Cross, Regent Street (JDW) White Horse, Gilda Brook Road (Private)
Irlam	❯	Tesco Store, Fairhills Ind. Estate (Tesco) Railway Inn, Liverpool Road (Private)
Peel Green	❯	Eccles Rugby Club (Private)
Salford	❯	Salford Museum & Gallery (Museum hrs) Mothercare, West One Retail Park (Private) Salford Central Station (Northern Rail) Salford Crescent Station (Northern Rail) Quay House Beefeater The Quays (Private) Salford City Reds Stadium, Willows Road (RFLC)
Swinton	❯	Pendleton Gateway Centre (Centre hrs) Salford Shopping City (Private)

Victoria Park, Pavilion (Pavilion hrs)
New Ellesmere, East Lancs Road (Private)
Swinton Free House, Chorley Road (Private)

Walkden ❯ Walkden Gateway Centre (Centre hrs)
Tesco Store, Ellesmere Shopping Centre (Tesco)

Worsley ❯ Barton Arms, Stable Fold (Private)
Moorings, Quayside Close, Boothstown (Private)

SEFTON

Ainsdale ❯ The Railway, Liverpool Road (Private)

Blundellsands ❯ Burbo Bank

Bootle ❯ Bootle Bus Station (Merseytravel)
New Strand Shopping Centre (Private)
Merton Inn, Merton Road (JDW)
The Wild Rose, Triad Centre (JDW)
Yates's Bar, Triad Centre (Yates)

Churchtown ❯ Preston New Road

Crosby ❯ Moor Lane

Formby ❯ Chapel Lane
Freshfield Car Park (National Trust)

Maghull ❯ Leighton Avenue
Coach & Horses, Liverpool Rd North (Private)

Southport ❯ Eastbank Street
Market Street (08.00-19.00)
Park Crescent, Hesketh Bank

Promenade Central ❯ Ocean Plaza, Marine Drive (Private)
Pleasureland (5) (Private)
Nandos, 7 Ocean Plaza (Nandos)
Sir Henry Segrave, Lord Street (JDW)
Willow Grove, Lord Street (JDW)
Yates's Bar, Lord Street (Yates)
Esplanade Caravan Club Site (Caravan Club)

SOUTH LAKELAND

Aldingham ❯ Church Car Park, Foreshore

Ambleside ❯ Mechanics Institute (Daytime)
Rothay Park (March-November)
Rydal Road Car Park
Waterhead Car Park

Arnside ❯ Promenade Shelter

Broughton-in-Furness ❯ The Square

Brown Howe ❯ South of Torver, nr. Lake Coniston (National Park)

Coniston ❯ Tilberthwaite Avenue Car Park
Park Coppice Caravan Club Site
(Caravan Club)

Dent ❯ Car Park (Parish Council)

Grange-over-Sands ❯ Berners Close Car Park
Fernleigh Road
Meathop Fell Caravan Club Site (Caravan Club)

Grasmere ❯ Moss Parrock, Village Centre

Hawkshead ❯ Car Park, Main Street

Kendal ❯ New Road Car Park
Peppercorn Lane
Miles Thompson, Allhallows Lane (JDW)

Kirkby Lonsdale ❯ Jingling Lane

Milnthorpe ❯ The Square

Monk Coniston ❯ N end of Lake (National Park)

Oxenholme ❯ Oxenholm Station, Platform 1 (Virgin)

Sedbergh ❯ Market Place, Joss Lane

Sedgwick ❯ Low Park Wood Caravan Club Site
(Caravan Club)

Staveley	⊗	Abbey Square
Ulverston	⊗	Brogden Street (Daytime) Canal Foot, Estuary Shore Croftlands/Priory Road (Daytime) Gill Car Park (Daytime) Market Hall (Daytime, not Wednesday or Sunday)
Windermere	⊗	Baddeley Clock Bowness Bay, Glebe Road Braithwaite Fold Car Park (Mid-March-Oct) Broad Street Car Park Ferry Nab Car Park Rayrigg Road Car Park Braithwaite Fold Caravan Club Site (Caravan Club) White Cross Bay Leisure Park (Private)

SOUTH RIBBLE

Bamber Bridge	⊗	Withy Grove, by Supermarket (Daytime) Millers, Lostock Lane (Private)
Lostock Hall	⊗	Hope Terrace, behind shops (Daytime)

STOCKPORT

Bramhall	⊗	Ack Lane East Village Square, Ack Lane (Private) Bramhall Station (Northern Rail)
Cheadle	⊗	Massie Street Car Park Bar SH, High Street (Private) The Weavers, Gatley Road (Private)
Cheadle Hulme	⊗	Kings Hall, Station Road (JDW) John Millington, Station Road (Private)
Compstall	⊗	Etheron Park Café, George St (Private)
Edgeley	⊗	Bulkeley Road Edgeley Library (Library hrs)
Great Moor	⊗	Great Moor Library (Library hrs)

Hazel Grove ❯ Hazel Grove Library (Library hrs)
Lyme Street
Torkington Park
Fiveways Hotel, Macclesfield Rd (Private)
Phoenix, London Road (Private)

Heald Green ❯ Heald Green Library (Library hrs)
Griffin, Wilmslow Road (Holts)

Heaton Moor ❯ Thornfield Park (Park hrs)
Elizabethan, Heaton Moor Lane (Private)
Moortop, Heaton Moor Road (Private)

High Lane ❯ High Lane Library (Library hrs)

Marple ❯ Derby Street, Car Park
Marple Library (Library hrs)
Memorial Park
Old Know Road
Rose Hill

Reddish ❯ Reddish Road
Reddish Library (Library hrs)
Carousel, Reddish Road (Private)

Romiley ❯ Forum Car Park, Compsall Road

Stockport ❯ Bridgefield Street
Bus Station, Daw Bank
Vernon Park, Turncroft Lane (Park hrs)
Merseyway Shopping Precinct
Debenhams Store, Princes Street (Debenhams)
Norwest Co-op Store, Chestergate (Private)
Sunwin Store, Chestergate (Private)
Stockport Station (Virgin)
Stockport College, Town Centre Campus
(College)
Calverts Court, St Petersgate (JDW)
Chestergate Tavern, Mersey Square (Private)
George & Dragon, Manchester Road (Private)
Pizza Hut, Wellington Road (Private)
Toby Carvery, Wellington Road (Private)
Grand Central Swimming Pool (Pool hrs) (Private)

Woodley ❯ Woodley Precinct

TAMESIDE

Ashton-under-Lyne ❯ Market Hall, Market Square (Hall hrs)
Ashton Bus Station (GMPTE)
Ashton-under-Lyne Station (Northern Rail)
Ash Tree, Wellington Road (JDW)
Nandos, Ashton Leisure Park (Nandos)
Gala Bingo, Wellington Road (Gala)

Denton ❯ Albert Street, by Market
Festival Hall (Hall hrs)

Droylsden ❯ Market Street/Greenside Lane

Hyde ❯ Clarendon Square (Shopping hrs)
Hyde Bus Station (GMPTE)
Cotton Bale, Market Place (JDW)

Mossley ❯ Market Ground, Stamford Street

Mottram ❯ Mottram Wood, Stockport Road (Private)

Stalybridge ❯ Armentieres Square, Trinity Street
Society Rooms, Grosvenor Street (JDW)
Greenwood Street (9.15-17.30)
John Leigh Park (Park Hrs)
Regent Road Car Park (Mon-Sat, 9.15-17.30)
Griffin, Stamford Road, Bowden (Private)

Dunham Massey ❯ Axe & Cleaver, School Lane (Private)

Hale ❯ Cecil Road, Car Park (9.00-17.00)

Sale ❯ Hereford Street (9.15-17.30)
Woodheys Park (Park hrs)
Worthington Park (Park hrs)
J P Joule, Northenden Road (JDW)
Sale Hotel, Marsland Road (Private)

Stretford ❯ Longford Park (Park hrs)
Bishop Blaize, Chester Road (JDW)

Trafford Centre ❯ Trafford Centre (Private) (CP)
Debenhams Store, Regent Cres (Debenhams)
Ha! Ha! Bar, The Orient (Private)
Nandos, 15 The Orient (Nandos)

Trafford Park ❯ 3rd Avenue (9.00-17.00)
Castle in the Air, Chill Factor Centre (JDW)

Urmston ❯ Moorfield Walk (9.15-17.30)
Tim Bobbin, Flixton Road (JDW)

WARRINGTON

Birchwood ❯ Birchwood Shopping Centre (Private)
Birchwood Station (Transpennine)

Higher Walton ❯ Walton Hall Gardens, Park Entrance (CP)
Walton Arms, Old Chester Road (Private)

Latchford ❯ Latchford Village

Lymm ❯ Church Green

❯ Pepper Street

Lymm M6 ❯ Lymm Services J20 M6 (Moto)

Stockton Heath ❯ Forge Car Park [Closure planned]
Nandos, 109 London Road (Nandos)

Stretton ❯ Cat & Lion, Tarporley Road (Private)
Hollow Tree, Tarporley Road (Private)

Warburton ❯ Saracens Head, Paddock Lane (Private)

Warrington ❯ Warrington Market (9.00-17.00, Mon-Sat)
Warrington Bus Station (8.30-23.00 Mon-Sat) CP
Golden Square MSCP (Private)
Golden Square Centre (Private)
Lyme Street (Private)
Warrington Bank Quay Station, Platform 2 (Virgin)
Friar Penketh, Barbauld Street (JDW)
Nandos, Old Market Square (Nandos)
Yates's Bar, Buttermarket Street (Yates)
Gala Bingo, Cockhedge Centre (Gala)

Winwick ❯ Swan, Golborne Road (Private)

WEST LANCASHIRE

Burscough ❯ School Lane, Car Park

Ormskirk ❯ Bus/Rail Interchange (CP)
Church Walks
Moor Street
Moorgate, opp. Indoor Market
Park Road, in Park
Shopmobility Office, Park Road (Private)

Parbold ❯ Parbold Station (Northern Rail)

Skelmersdale ❯ Concourse Shopping Centre (2) (Private)

Tarleton ❯ Church Road, Car Park

WIGAN

Ashton-in-Makerfield ❯ Princess Road (8.00-17.00)
Bay Horse, Warrington Road (Private)
Sir Thomas Gerard, Gerard Street (JDW)

Goose Green ❯ Venture, Billinge Road (Private)

Leigh ❯ Bengal Street (8.00-17.00)
Bus Station, King Street (8.00-17.00)
Thomas Burke, Leigh Road (JDW)

Standish ❯ Charnley Arms, Almond Brook Road (Private)

Wigan ❯ Bus Station, Hallgate
Town Hall (8.45-16.30)
The Galleries, Hindley Walk (Private)
Grand Arcade Shopping Centre (Private)
Wigan North Western Station, Subway (Virgin)
Wigan Wallgate Station (Northern Rail)
Brocket Arms, Mesnes Road (JDW)
Moon Under Water, Market Place (JDW)
Walkabout, King Street (Private)
Gala Bingo, Robin Park (Gala)
Robin Park Sports Complex (Private)

Worthington Lakes ❯ Visitor Centre (Utd Utilities)

WIRRAL

Bebington ❯ Bebington Civic Centre (Centre hrs)
Bebington One Stop Shop (Office hrs)
Higher Bebington Library (Library hrs)

Birkenhead ❯ Cheshire Lines Building (Office hrs)
Claughton Road Bus Station
Conway One Stop Shop (Office hrs)
Shopmobility Centre
Westminster House (Office hrs)
Wirral Museum (Museum hrs)
Woodside Bus Station
Birkenhead Park Station (Merseyrail)
Brass Balance, Argyle Street (JDW)
The John Laird, Europa Centre (JDW)
Yates's Bar, Exmouth Street (Yates)

Bromborough ❯ Bromborough Civic Centre (Centre hrs)
Gala Bingo, Wirral Leisureland (Gala)

Eastham ❯ Eastham Country Park
Eastham One Stop Shop (Office hrs)

Heswall ❯ Heswall Library & One Stop Shop (Office hrs)

Hoylake ❯ Hoylake Station
Meols Parade Gardens, by bowling greem
Hoylake Lights, Market Street (JDW)

Greasby
Irby ❯ Greasby Library (Library hrs)
Irby Library (Library hrs)

Landican ❯ Landican Cemetery

Meols ❯ Bennetts Lane, Meols Parade

Moreton ❯ Leasowe Common
Moreton Cross, Garden Lane
Moreton One Stop Shop (Office hrs)
Grange, Hoylake Road (Private)
Mockbeggar Hall, Hoylake Road (JDW)

New Brighton ❯ Harrison Drive
Kings Parade, Marine Promenade
New Brighton One Stop Shop (Office hrs)

New Ferry	❯	Woodhead Street car park John Masefield (JDW)
Prenton	❯	Prenton Library (Library hrs)
Rock Ferry	❯	Rock Ferry One Stop Shop (Office hrs)
Thornton Hough	❯	Thornton Common Road
Thurstaston	❯	Wirral Country Park Visitor Centre (Centre hrs) Wirral Country Park Caravan Club Site (Caravan Club)
Upton	❯	Upton Library (Library hrs)
Wallasey	❯	Cherrytree Centre (Centre hrs) Shopmobilty Centre (Centre hrs) Liscard One Stop Shop (Office hrs) Seacombe Library (Library hrs) Wallasey Central Library (Library hrs) Wallasey Town Hall (Office hrs) Clairville, Wallasey Road (JDW)
West Kirby	❯	Dee Lane, West Kirby Lakes Grange Road, by Station West Kirby Concourse (Centre hrs) Dee Hotel, Grange Road (JDW)
Woodchurch	❯	Woodchurch Library (Library hrs)

WYRE

Cleveleys	❯	Café, North Promenade Car Park, Rough Lea Road North Drive
Fleetwood	❯	Beach Road, by Cemetery Bold Street, Euston Park Marine Hall Car Park Memorial Park Preston Street Thomas Drummond, London St (JDW)
Garstang	❯	High Street, Community Centre Car Park Park Hill Road Car Park

Great Eccleston ❯ The Weind, off High Street

Knott End ❯ Barton Square
Quail Holme Road Car Park

Pilling ❯ School Lane

Poulton ❯ Teanlowe Centre, Queensway
United Reformed Church, Titebarn Street
(Church) (CP)
Poulton-le-Fylde Station (Northern Rail)

Scorton ❯ Gubberford Lane

Thornton ❯ Stannah Country Park
Shopping Precinct, Victoria Rd East

YORKSHIRE

BARNSLEY

Barnsley ◉ Cheapside
Barnsley Town Hall (Office hrs) (CP)
Metropolitan Shopping Centre (Private)
Barnsley Station (SYPTE)
Escapade, Wellington Street (2) (Private)
Heart of Barnsley, Peel Street (Marstons)
Joseph Brammahs, Market Hill (JDW)
Silkstone Inn, Market Street (JDW)
Walkabout, Church Street (Private)
White Bear, Church Street (Private)
Yates's Bar, Shambles Street (Yates)
Parkway Cinema, Eldon Street (Private)

Cudworth ◉ Barnsley Road
Fayre & Square, Darfield Road (Private)

Goldthorpe ◉ Barnsley Road

Monk Bretton ◉ Norman Inn, Burton Road (Private)

Wombwell ◉ High Street
The Horseshoe, High Street (JDW)

BRADFORD

Bingley ◉ Market, Chapel Lane
Midland Hotel, Main Street (Private)
Myrtle Grove, Main Street (JDW)

Bradford ◉ Bradford Central Library (Library hrs) (CP)
City Hall, Bradford Centre (M&F)
Lister Park (Park hrs)
Centenary Square (Private)
Kirkgate Shopping Centre (Private)
Oastler Shopping Centre (Private)
Ladbrokes, Lillycroft Road (Private)
Bradford Interchange Bus Station (WYMetro)
Bradford Forster Sq. Station (Northern Rail)
Bar:Me, Great Horton Rd (Private)
City Vaults, Hustlergate (Private)
Goose on Bridge Street, Bridge Street (M&B)

Manor House, Leeds Road (Private)
Markaz Restaurant, Cemtenary Sq (Private)
Nandos, The Leisure Exchange (Nandos)
Sir Titus Salt, Morley Street (JDW)
Turls Green, Centenary Square (JDW)
Unicorn, Ivegate (Private)
Walkabout, Glydegate Street (Private)
Varsity, Great Horton St (Barracuda)
Yates's Bar, Queensgate (Yates)
Gala Bingo, Tong Street (Gala)
Carlisle Business Centre (Private) CP
Bradford College, Gt. Horton Street (College)
University of Bradford, Richmond Building
(University) (CP)

Burley-in-Wharfedale ❯ Station Road

East Bowling ❯ Bowling Pool, Flockton Road (CP)

Eccleshill ❯ Eccleshill Leisure Centre, Harrogate Road (CP)

Esholt ❯ Car Park, Station Road

Guiseley ❯ Guiseley Station (Northern Rail)

Harden ❯ St Ives Estate Car Park

Haworth ❯ Bronte Parsonage Car Park (M&F)
Central Park, Rawdon Road
Penistone Hill Country Park (M&F) (Summer)

Idle ❯ Hitching Post, Leeds Road (Marstons)

Ilkley ❯ Central Car Park, Brooke Street
Riverside, Bridge House Lane (M&F)
White Wells
Ilkley Pool & Lido (CP)
Hare & Hounds, Menston (Private)

Keighley ❯ Cavendish Street
Keighley Market
Keighley Leisure Centre (CP)
Bus Station, Towngate (WYMetro)
Livery Rooms, North Street (JDW)
Gala Bingo, Alice Street (Gala)
Keighley Bowl, Alston Retail Park (AMF)

Menston	◉	Hare & Hounds, Bradford Road (Private)
Odsall	◉	Grattan Stadium (Bradford Bulls)
Saltaire	◉	Caroline Street (M&F)
Shipley	◉	Market Square Lloyds Bar, Market Square (JDW)
Silsden		Car Park, Bridge Street
Thornbury	◉	The Farmers, Bradford Road (Private)
Thornton	◉	Thornton Recreation Centre (CP)
Wibsey	◉	Ancient Foresters, High Street (Private)
Wilsden	◉	Prune Park Bar (Private)

CALDERDALE

Brighouse	◉	Thornton Square (6.00-18.00) Richard Ostler, Bethal Street (JDW) Holiday Inn Health Club, Clifton Village (Private)
Elland	◉	Market Square (Market hrs) Town Hall Square (6.00-18.00)
Halifax	◉	Albion Street (Mon-Sat, Daytime) Borough Market (Market hrs) George Square (6.00-18.00) Manor Heath Park (8.00-15.00) North Bridge Leisure Centre (Centre hrs) Ogden Water Country Park Piece Hall (2) (Daytime) Savile Park, Skircoat Halifax Bus Station (WYMetro) Halifax Station, Platform 2 (Northern Rail) Barracuda Bar, Bull Green (Barracuda) Barun Top Inn, Rawson Street (JDW) Caffe Nero, Southgate (Caffe Nero) Goose at the Arcade, Commercial Street (M&B) Millers, Salterhebble Hill (Private) The Shay Stadium (2) (Halifax Town FC)
Hebden Bridge	◉	Calder Holmes Park (Summer, Park hrs)

Market Square (Market hrs)
Midgehole, Hardcastle Craggs (Apr-Sept) [Ambulant only]
New Road (06.00-18.00)
Valley Road (6.00-18.00)
Hebden Bridge Station (Northern Rail) [Planned]

Heptonstall	❯	Towngate Car Park
Luddenden	❯	Luddenden Lane (6.00-18.00)
Mytholmroyd	❯	Bridge End (6.00-18.00)
Ripponden	❯	Brig Royd
Sowerby Bridge	❯	Wharf Street Car Park (6.00-18.00)
Shibden	❯	Shibden Hall (10.00-16.30)
		Shibden Park Playground (Park hrs)
Todmorden	❯	Brook Street (6.00-18.00)
		Centre Vale Park, Burnley Rd (Daytime)
		Market Hall (Market hrs)

CRAVEN

Bolton Abbey	❯	Strid Wood Caravan Club Site (Caravan Club)
Buckden	❯	Car Park (Yorks. Dales NP)
Clapham	❯	Car Park (Yorks. Dales NP)
Gargrave	❯	High Street/South Street (Dawn-Dusk)
Glusburn	❯	Main Street
Grassington	❯	Car Park (Yorks. Dales NP)
Horton-in-Ribblesdale	❯	Car Park (Yorks. Dales NP)
Ingleton	❯	Community Centre Car Park (Parish Council)
Kettlewell	❯	Car Park (Yorks. Dales NP)
Malham	❯	Car Park (Yorks. Dales NP)

Settle	⟩	Ashfield Car Park
		Whitefriars Car Park
Skipton	⟩	Bus Station
		High St Car Park (8.00-18.00)
		Town Hall (Office hrs)
		Skipton Station (2) (Northern Rail)
		Devonshire, Newmarket Street (JDW)
Stainforth	⟩	Car Park (Yorks. Dales NP)
Threshfield	⟩	Wharfedale Caravan Club Site (Caravan Club)

DONCASTER

Adwick	⟩	Adwick Station (Northern Rail)
Bawtry	⟩	Gainsborough Road
Bentley	⟩	Bentley Park Gates, Cooke Street
Conisbrough	⟩	Church Street
Doncaster	⟩	Council House, College Rd (Office hrs)
		Market Place, High Fishergate (7.00-17.00)
		Southern Bus Station (7.30-17.30)
		Frenchgate Centre (11) (Private)
		Doncaster Station, Platform 8&3A (East Coast)
		Che Bar, Silver Street (Private)
		Gatehouse, Priory Walk (JDW)
		Old Angel, Cleveland Street (JDW)
		Red Lion, Market Place (JDW)
		Walkabout, Priory Walk (Private)
Hatfield M18	⟩	Doncaster North Services, J5 M18 (Moto)
High Melton	⟩	Doncaster College, University Centre (College)
Mexborough	⟩	Market Street, opp. Fish Market
		Old Market Hall, Market Street (JDW)
Moorends	⟩	Wembley Road
Thorne	⟩	The Green, Finkle Street

Tickhill → The Library (Library hrs)

EAST RIDING OF YORKSHIRE

Beverley → Dyer Lane (Daytime)
Lord Roberts Road (Daytime)
Sow Hill Bus Station (Daytime)
Station Square

Bridlington → Beaconsfield Promenade (Daytime)
Belvedere Parade, Boat Compound (Summer)
Coach Park, Hilderthorpe Road (Daytime)
Limekiln Lane (Daytime)
Princess Mary Promenade (Daytime)
Queen Street
Royal Princess Parade (Daytime)
South Cliff Gardens
South Marine Drive (Summer, Daytime)
The Promenades (Private)
Bridlington Station (Northern Rail)
Prior John, Promenade (JDW)
Gala Bingo, Promenade (Gala)

Yorkshire

Yorkshire

Brough	⊙	Ferry Inn, Station Road (Marstons)
Cottingham	⊙	Market Green (Daytime)
Driffield	⊙	Cross Hill (Town Council) North Street (Town Council)
Flamborough	⊙	Lighthouse (Daytime)
Goole	⊙	Escourt Street (Daytime) City & County, Market Square (JDW)
Hedon	⊙	Watmoughs Arcade (Daytime)
Hessle	⊙	Cliff Road, Hessle Mill (Daytime) The Square (Daytime) Humber Bridge Car Park (Bridge Board)
Hornsea	⊙	Boat Compound (Summer) Cinema Street (Daytime) Marine Drive (Daytime)
Howden	⊙	St Helens Square (Daytime)
Kilnsea	⊙	Seaside Road Car Park (Daytime)
Mappleton	⊙	Cliff Road Car Park (Daytime)
Market Weighton	⊙	Londesborough Road (Daytime)
North Ferriby	⊙	Duke of Cumberland, High St. (Marstons)
Pocklington	⊙	Railway Street (Daytime)
Sewerby	⊙	Sewerby Park (Summer) Sewerby Cricket Club, by Pavilion (Daytime)
Stamford Bridge	⊙	The Square
Withernsea	⊙	Central Promenade (Daytime) Piggy Lane (Daytime)

HAMBLETON

Bedale	◉	Bridge Street Car Park
Chopgate	◉	Car Park (North York Moors NP)
Easingwold	◉	Market Place
Great Ayton	◉	Park Rise, off High Street
Kildale	◉	Kildale Station
		Car Park (North York Moors NP)
Northallerton	◉	Applegarth Car Park (8.00-19.00)
Osmotherly	◉	South End/School Lane
Stokesley	◉	High Street
Sutton Bank	◉	Visitor Centre (North York Moors NP)
Swainby	◉	-
Thirsk	◉	Market Place
		Millgate Car Park
		Thirsk Station (Transpennine)
		Three Tuns, Market Place (JDW)

HARROGATE

Beckwithshaw	◉	Smiths Arms, Church Row (Private)
Boroughbridge	◉	Back Lane Car Park
Harrogate	◉	Crescent Gardens, Crescent Road
		Devonshire Place, Skipton Road
		Jubilee MSCP
		Library Gardens, Victoria Avenue
		Oatlands Recreation Ground, Hookstone Rd
		Starbeck High Street
		Stray Ponds, York Place
		Tower Street MSCP
		Valley Gardens
		Victoria MSCP
		Victoria Shopping Centre (Private)
		Harrogate Station (Northern Rail)
		Asda Store, Bower Road (Asda)
		Winter Gardens, Royal Baths (JDW)

Knaresborough	◉	Bond End, High Street
		Bus Station
		Castle Yard
		Conyngham Hall Car Park
		York Place Car Park
		Knaresborough Caravan Club Site
		(Caravan Club)
Masham	◉	Dixon Keld, nr. Police Station
Pateley Bridge	◉	Recreation Ground
		Southlands Car Park
Ripley	◉	Visitors Car Park
Ripon	◉	Bus Station
		Minster Road
		Spa Gardens
		Wakemans House, High Skellgate
Sickinghall	◉	Scotts Arms, Main Street (Private)

KINGSTON-UPON-HULL

Hull

Albert Avenue Pools (Centre hrs)
Costello Athletics Stadium (Stadium hrs)
Guildhall Square
Holderness Road, by East Park
Hull Arena (Arena hrs)
Hull Central Library (Library hrs)
West Park (Park hrs)
Woodford Leisure (Centre hrs)
Goodwin Centre, Guildhall Road (CP)
North Point Shopping Centre (Private)
Princes Quay Shopping Centre (Private)
Prospect Shopping Centre (Private)
Trinity Market. North Church Side (Private)
Debenhams Store, Prospect St. (Debenhams)
Admiral of the Humber, Anlaby Rd (JDW)
Apollo, Holderness High Road (Marstons)
Bridges, Suitton Road (Private)
Biarritz, George Street (Marstons)
Goodfellowship, Cottingham Rd (Marstons)
Highway, Willerby Road (Marstons)
Hog's Head, Whitefriargate (Private)
Hull Cheese, Paragon Street (Private)
Linnet & Lark, Princess Ave (Marstons)
Lyrics, Whitefriargate (Private)
Mainbrace, Beverley Road (Private)
Nandos, St Stephens Centre (Nando)
Oystercatcher, Kingswood Leisure Park (Private)
Parkers, Anlaby Road (Private)
Priory Inn, Priory Road (Marstons)
Revolution, Lowgate (Private)
Sutton Fields, Oslo Road (M&B)
3 John Scotts, Alfred Gelder Street (JDW)
White Horse, Carr Lane (Private)
William Wilberforce, Trinity House Lane (JDW)
Zachariah Pearson, Beverley Road (JDW)
Gala Bingo, Oslo Road (Gala)
Mecca Bingo, Anlaby Road (Mecca)
Odeon Cinema, Kingston Retail Park (Odeon)

KIRKLEES

Batley

Batley Town Hall (Office hrs)

Market Square
Wilton Park (Park hrs)
Union Rooms, Hick Lane (JDW)

Birstall ❯ Oakwell Hall Information Centre
Town Centre
Nandos, Gelderd Road (Nandos)

Cleckheaton ❯ Cleckheaton Town Hall (Office hrs)
Market Arcade
Obediah Brooke, Bradford Road (JDW)

Dewsbury ❯ Crow Nest Park (Park hrs)
Dewsbury Library (Library hrs)
Dewsbury Museum (Museum hrs)
Dewsbury Town Hall (Office hrs)
Longcauseway, Market Place
Social Services Information Point
Dewsbury Bus Station (WYMetro)
The Principle, Northgate (Barracuda)
West Riding, by Station (Private)
The Time Piece, Northgate (JDW)

Fartown ❯ Birkby & Fartown Library (Library hrs)

Fenay Bridge ❯ Fenay Bridge, Penistone Road (Private)

Heckmondwike ❯ Heckmondwike Market
Oldfield Lane

Holme ❯ Village Centre

Holmfirth ❯ Bus Station, Towngate

Honley ❯ Moorbottom

Huddersfield ❯ Albion Street, Civic Centre Car Park
Civic Centre 1 (Office hrs)
Greenhead Park (Park hrs)
Huddersfield Library & Art Gallery (Library hrs)
Huddersfield Open Market
Library (Library hrs)
Queensgate Market
Town Hall (Office hrs)
The Media Centre (Private)
Bus Station, Albion Street (WYMetro)

Huddersfield Station (Transpennine)
Beatties Store, Kingsgate Centre (Private)
Caffe Nero, King Street (Caffe Nero)
Cherry Tree, John William Street (JDW)
Court House, Queens Street (Private)
Lord Wilson, King Street (JDW)
Nandos, John William Street (Nandos)
Varsity, Zetland Street (Barracuda)
Warehouse, Zetland Street (Private)
Yates's Bar, King Street (Yates)

Marsden ⊘ Peel Street

Marsh ⊘ Westbourne Road

Milnsbridge ⊘ Morley Lane

Mirfield ⊘ Knowle Park
Station Road

New Mill ⊘ Holmfirth Road

Outlane ⊘ Waggon & Horses, New Hay Lane (Private)

Ravensknowle ⊘ Tolson Museum (Museum hrs)

Slaithwaite ⊘ Carr Lane

LEEDS

Armley ⊘ Theaker Lane

Boston Spa ⊘ Village Hall, High St. (Parish Council)

Bramhope Golden Acre Park (Park hrs)
Old Lane Car Park

Bramley ⊘ Town Street

Chapel Allerton ⊘ Three Hulats, Harrogate Road (JDW)

Cottingley ⊘ Cottingley Hall Crematorium (Crematorium hrs)

Crossgates ⊘ Crossgates Library (Library hrs)
Cross Gates Shopping Centre (Private)

Garforth	⊘	Barleyhill Road
Gildersome	⊘	Gildersome Library (Library hrs)

Headingley ⊘ Ash Road/North Lane
Carnegie Stadium, S. Stand (Leeds Rugby)
Headingley Stadium (Yorkshire CCC)

Horsforth ⊘ Horsforth Library (Library hrs)
Horsforth Station (Northern Rail)

Leeds ⊘ County Arcade, Vicar Lane
Kirkgate Market, Vicar Lane
St John's Centre, Albion Street/Merrion Street
The Corn Exchange, Call Lane (Private)
Headrow Shopping Centre (Private)
The Light, The Headrow (2) (Private)
Trinity Leeds [Planned} (CP)
Debenhams Store, Briggate (Debenhams)
Debenhams Store, White Rose (Debenhams)
Leeds City Bus Station (WYMetro)
Leeds Station (3) (Network Rail)
West Yorkshire Playhouse (Private)
Beckets Bank, Park Row (JDW)
Bourbon, Cookridge Street (Private)
Browns, The Headrow (M&B)
The Courtyard, Cookridge Street (Private)
Cuthbert Brodrick, Portland Crescent (JDW)
Edwards, Merrion Street (M&B)
Ha! Ha! Bar, Millennium Square (Private)
Hog's Head, Great George Street (Private)
J D Wetherpoon, Leeds Station (JDW)
Japanic, Clay Pit Lane (Private)
Jongleurs, The Cube (Private)
Majestyk, City Square (Private)
McDonalds, Briggate (McDonalds)
McDonalds, St Johns Shopping Centre
(McDonalds)
Nandos, 152 Briggate (Nandos)
Nandos, Cardigan Fields (Nandos)
Nandos, The Light (Nandos)
Packhorse, Briggate (Private)
Prohibition, Greek Street (Private)
Qube, Portland Crescent (Private)
Quid Pro Quo, Greek Street (Private)
Revolution, Cookridge Street (Private)

Slug & Lettuce, Park Road (Private)
Squares, Boar Lane (Private)
Stick or Twist, The Podium (JDW)
Tampopo, South Parade (Private)
Toad at the Firehouse, East Parade (Private)
Varsity, Woodhouse Lane (Barracuda)
Walkabout, Cookridge Street (Private)
The Wellington, Wellington Street (Private)
Wetherspoons, City Station (JDW)
Yates's Bar, Boar Lane (Yates)
Yates's Bar, Woodhouse Lane (Yates)
Elland Road Stadium (Leeds Utd)
West Yorkshire Playhouse, Quarry Hill (Private)

Moor Allerton   ❯   Penny Fun, Shopping Centre (Private)

Morley   ❯   Morley Town Hall (Office hrs)
Wesley Street/Queen Street

Osmondthorpe   ❯   Osmondthorpe Library/One Stop Centre
(Centre hrs)

Otley   ❯   Chevin Forest Park, by Study Centre
Nelson Street, Visitors Centre & Library

Pudsey   ❯   Market Place

Rothwell   ❯   Marsh Street, Car Park

Roundhay   ❯   Tropical World (Park hrs)

Wetherby   ❯   The Shambles, Cross Street
Wetherby Services, A1(M) Junct 46 (Moto)

RICHMONDSHIRE

Askrigg   ❯   Village Hall (Hall hrs)

Aysgarth Falls   ❯   Car Park (Yorks. Dales NP)

Bainbridge   ❯   -

Catterick Village   ❯   Bank Yard

Colburn   ❯   Broadway

Grinton	⊙	-
Gunnerside	⊙	-
Hawes	⊙	Market Place Car Park (Yorks. Dales NP) Brown Moor Caravan Club Site (Caravan Club)
Hipswell	⊙	Hildyard Row/White Shops
Keld	⊙	-
Langthwaite	⊙	-
Leyburn	⊙	Kelberdale Railway Street Lower Wesleydale Caravan Club Site (Caravan Club)
Middleham	⊙	-
Muker	⊙	-
Reeth	⊙	-
Richmond	⊙	The Falls Nuns Close Car Park Reeth Road Cemetery Ronaldshay Park Round House Victoria Road Ralph Fitz Randell, Queens Road (JDW) Hargill House Caravan Club Site (Caravan Club)

ROTHERHAM

Aston-cumAughton	⊙	Leisure Centre (Centre hrs)
East Dene	⊙	Mowbray Gardens Library(Library hrs)
Greasbrough	⊙	Greasbrough Library (Library hrs)
Maltby	⊙	Joint Customer Care Centre (Centre hrs) Leisure Centre (Centre hrs) [2010]

Rotherham ❯ All Saints Square (Daytime)
Centenary Market Hall Entrance (Market hrs)
Clifton Park Museum, Clifton Lane (Museum hrs)
Clifton Park Wet Play Area (Park hrs) (CP)
St Ann's Leisure Centre (Centre hrs)
Rotherham Central Station (Northern Rail)
The Blue Coat, The Crofts (JDW)
Corn Law Rhymer, High Street (JDW)
The Rhinoceros, Bridgegate (JDW)

Thrybergh ❯ Country Park, Anglers' Lodge

Wath-upon-Dearn ❯ Church House, Montgomery Square (JDW)

RYEDALE

Danby ❯ The Moors Centre (North York Moors NP)

Grosmont ❯ Grosmont Station (N York Moors Rlwy)

Helmsley ❯ Borogate
Cleveland Way Car Park

Hutton-le-Hole ❯ Car Park (North York Moors NP)

Kirkbymoorside ❯ Town Farm Car Park

Malton ❯ Market Place

Norton ❯ Church Street

Pickering ❯ Eastgate
The Ropery Car Park
Pickering Station (N York Moors Rlwy)

Rosedale ❯ Rosedale Abbey

Staxton ❯ Saxton Brow Picnic Area

Thornton-le-Dale ❯ Lakeside Car Park

SCARBOROUGH

Filey ❯ The Beach (Easter-October)

		Ravine, Cobble Landing
		Royal Parade
		Station Avenue Car Park
Glaisdale	❯	Station Car Park
Goathland	❯	Car Park (North York Moors NP)
		Goathland Station (NYMR)
Grosmont	❯	Front Street
Ravenscar	❯	Raven Hall Road (North York Moors NP)
Robin Hood's Bay	❯	Station Car Park (Summer)
Scaling Dam	❯	Car Park (North York Moors NP)
Scarborough	❯	Burniston Road Car Park
		North Bay (Easter-Oct)
		Peasholme Park
		Royal Albert Drive, North Bay
		South Cliff Gardens, nr. Spa (Easter-Oct)
		Sports Centre (Centre hrs)
		St Helens Square
		St Nicholas, Foreshore (Easter-Oct)
		Weaponess Coach Park
		West Pier
		Brunswick Shopping Centre (Private)
		Debenhams Store, Brunswick Pavilion
		(Debenhams)
		Scarborough Station, Platform 3 (Transpennine)
		Lord Rosebery, Westborough (JDW)
		The West Riding, Castle Road (M&B)
		Yates's Bar, St Nicholas Street (Yates)
Staithes	❯	Staithes Bank Bottom
		Staithes Top Car Park
West Ayton	❯	West Ayton Caravan Club Site (Caravan Club)
Whitby	❯	Abbey Headland, Car Park
		Kyber Pass, The Battery
		Marina, Car Park
		New Quay, New Quay Road
		North Promanade, The Beach
		West Cliff Beach (Easter-Oct)

SELBY

Barlow Common ⊘ Nature Reserve Visitor Centre (Centre hrs)

Selby ⊘ Abbey Leisure Centre (Centre hrs)
Back Micklegate Car Park
Park Street, by Selby Park
Morrisons Store, Market Cross (Morrison)
Tesco Store, Portholme Road (Tesco)

Sherburn-in-Elmet ⊘ Low Street

Tadcaster ⊘ Britannia Car Park

SHEFFIELD

Beighton ⊘ Belfry, Eckington Road (Private)

Chapeltown ⊘ Park Gates, Cowley Lane (Daytime)

Crystal Peaks ⊘ Crystal Peaks Shopping Centre (Private)

Foxhouse ⊘ Public House Car Park, Hathersage Road

Gleadless Town End ⊘ White Lane, opp Red Lion

Gower Street ⊘ Ellesmere Road Shops

For more information on
Public Facilities and access at
many attractions,
why not telephone for more
details before you travel?

*Please telephone for
all enquiries:*

SELBY
DISTRICT COUNCIL
Moving forward with purpose

01757
705101

Hillsborough ❯ Rawson Spring, Langsett Road (JDW)

Manor Top ❯ Ridgeway Rd/Mansfield Rd

Meadowhall ❯ Debenhams Store, Park Lane (Debenhams)
Meadowhall Station (SYPTE)
Nandos, The Oasis (Nandos)

Norton ❯ Main Road/Meadowhead

Rivelin ❯ Manchester Road/Rivelin Valley Road

Sheffield City Centre ❯ Angel Street
Moorfoot (Mon-Sat, 7.00-18.15)
Royal Hallamshire Hospital CP
Castle Market (Market hrs) (Private)
Orchard Square (Private)
Debenhams Store, The Moor (Debenhams)
Sheffield Station, Concourse & Platform 5
(E Midlands Trains)
Bankers Draft, Market Place (JDW)
Benjamin Huntsman, Cambridge Street (JDW)
Ha! Ha! Bar, St Pauls Parade (Private)
Nandos, West Street (Nandos)
Sheffield Waterworks Company, Division St (JDW)
Swim Inn, Glossop Road (JDW)
Varsity, Eccleshall Road (Barracuda)
Varsity, West Street (Barracuda)
Walkabout, Carver Street (Private)
Yates's Bar, Carver Street (Yates)
Bramall Lane Stadium (Sheffield Utd)
Crucible Theatre [Planned] (CP)

Stocksbridge ❯ Market Street

Valley Centertainment Centre ❯ Nandos, Broughton Lane (Nandos)

Wadsley Bridge ❯ opp. Shopping Precinct, Halifax Rd

Woodseats ❯ Abbey Lane CP
Woodseats Palace, Chesterfield Rd (JDW)

WAKEFIELD

Ackworth ⟩ Beverley Arms, Doncaster Rd (Marstons)

Castleford ⟩ Carlton Lane Shopping Centre (Private)
Castleford Bus Station (WYMetro)
Carltons, Carlton Street (Private)
Glass Blower, Bank Street (JDW)
Nandos, Xscape (Nandos)
Shout, Station Road (Private)
Winter Seam, Xscape (JDW)
Bowlplex, Xscape (Private)

Darrington ⟩ The Darrington, Gt. North Road (Private)

Hemsworth ⟩ Vale Head Sports Pavilion (Centre hrs)

Horbury ⟩ Horbury Library, Westfield Rd (Library hrs)
Old Mill, Wakefield Road (Private)

Knottingley M62 ⟩ Ferrybridge Services, J30 M62/A1 (Moto)

Ossett ⟩ Ossett Town Hall (Office hrs)

Pontefract ⟩ Pontefract Town Hall (Office hrs)
Pontefract Bus Station (WYMetro)
Red Lion, Market Place (Private)

Wakefield ⟩ The Springs
Wakefield Reference Library (Library hrs)
Wakefield Town Hall (Office hrs)
The Ridings Shopping Centre (2) (Private)
Caffe Nero, Kirkgate (Private)
The Gate, Northgate (Marstons)
Lupset Hotel, Horbury Road (Private)
Nandos, Westgate Retail Park (Nandos)
Quest, Westgate (Private)
Six Chimneys, Kirkgate (JDW)
Slug & Fiddle, Almsgate (Private)

West Bretton M1 ⟩ Woolley Edge Services, J38/39 M1 (Moto)

YORK

Acomb ⟩ Front Street (8.00-20.00)
Acomb Library (Library hrs) (CP)
Oaklands Leisure Centre [Planned] (CP)

Marcia Grey, Front Street (Private)

Clifton ◯ Homestead Park (Daytime) (Rowntree Trust)

Dringhouses ◯ Askham Bar Park & Ride

Fulford ◯ York Designer Outlet (Private)

Grimston ◯ Grimston Bar Park & Ride

Haxby ◯ Town Centre (8.00-20.00)

Rawcliffe ◯ Rawcliffe Bar Park & Ride

York ◯ Coppergate (8.00-20.00)
Kent Street, Car Park (8.00-20.00)
Museum Gardens (April-Sept)
Nunnery Lane, Car Park (8.00-20.00)
Parliament Street (8.00-20.00)
St George's Field (April-Sept)
St Leonards Place, Exhibition Square (8.00-20.00)
St Sampsons Square (8.00-20.00)
Silver Street [Planned] (CP)
Tanner Row (8.00-20.00)
Union Terrace, Car Park (8.00-20.00)
York Central Library (Library hrs)
Long Close Lane, Walmgate (CP)
York Station, Platforms 2 & 8 (East Coast)
Ha! Ha! Bar, New Street (Private)
Loch Fyne Restaurant", Walmgate (Private)
Nandos, High Ousegate (Nandos)
Old Orleans, Low Ousegate (Private)
Postern Gate, Piccadilly (JDW)
Punch Bowl, Blossom Street (JDW)
Royal York Hotel, Station Road (Private)
Slug & Lettuce, Low Ousegate (Private)
Varsity, 6-12 Lendal (Barracuda)
Windmill, Blossom Street (Private)
Yates's Bar, Low Ousegate (Yates)
City Screen, Coney Street (Private)
Mecca Bingo, Fishergate (Private)
York City Knights Rugby Stadium (Private)
York Race Course (Private)
Beechwood Grange Caravan Club Site (Caravan Club)
Rowntree Park Caravan Club Site (Caravan Club)

NORTH EAST ENGLAND

DARLINGTON

Darlington ❯ Horsemarket, by Shopmobility
Cornmill Shopping Centre (Private)
Darlington Station, Platform 4 (East Coast)
The Brinkburn, Lady Katherine Grove (Private)
The Mowden, Staindrop Road (M&B)
Tanners Hall, Skinnergate (JDW)
William Stead, Crown Street (JDW)
Yates's Bar, Skinnergate (Yates)
Gala Bingo, Skinnergate (Gala)

DURHAM

Allensford ❯ Allensford Caravan/Picnic Park, off A68

Barnard Castle ❯ Galgate Car Park

Bishop Auckland ❯ Bus Station
Stanley Jefferson, Market Place (JDW)

Chester-le-Street ❯ Foundry Lane (Mon-Sat, 9.00-17.00)
Riverside (Daytime)
Chester-le-Street Station (Northern Rail)
Wicket Gate, Front Street (JDW)

Consett ❯ Consett Bus Station, Medomsley Road

Crimdon ❯ Crimdon Park

Durham ❯ Milburngate Shopping Centre (Shopping hrs)
Walkergate Car Park (8.00-18.00)
Durham Station (East Coast)
Bishops Mill, Walkergate (JDW)
Hog's Head, Saddler Street (Private)
Nandos, Walkergate (Nandos)
Varsity, Saddler Street (Barracuda)
Walkabout, North Road (Private)
Water House, North Road (JDW)
Yates's Bar, North Road (Yates)
Grange Caravan Club Site (Caravan Club)

Easington ❯ Primary Care Offices, Seaside Lane (Office hrs)

Middleton-in-Teesdale	❯	-
Newton Aycliffe	❯	Newton Aycliffe Leisure Centre (Centre hrs)
Peterlee	❯	Peterlee Leisure Centre (Centre hrs) Five Quarter, Hailsham Place (JDW)
Seaham	❯	Seaham Hall Car Park Seaham Leisure Centre (Centre hrs) Town Centre Vane Tempest Car Park
Staindrop	❯	-
Stanhope	❯	Durham Dales Visitor Centre
Stanley	❯	Stanley Bus Station
Wearhead	❯	by Bridge

GATESHEAD

Birtley	❯	Harraton Terrace
Blaydon	❯	The Precinct
Gateshead	❯	Gateshead Shopping Centre (Private) Baja Beach Club, Pipewellgate (Private) Sage Gateshead (Private) (CP)
Lamesley	❯	Ravensworth Arms (Private)
Lowfell	❯	Lowerys Lane
MetroCentre	❯	MetroCentre (CP) Debenhams Store, Redpath Way (Debenhams) Nandos, Garden Walk (Nandos) Nandos, Russell Way (Nandos) Wetherspoons, MetroCentre (JDW) Gala Bingo, Metro Retail Park (Gala)
Whickham	❯	Woodmans Arms Whickham Park (Private)

HARTLEPOOL

Hartlepool ❯ Central Library, York Road, (Library hrs)
Place in the Park, Ward Jackson Park
(10.00-16.00)
Stockton Street Car Park (7.30-18.00)
Town Hall Theatre Foyer (Theatre hrs)
King John's Tavern, South Road (JDW)
Ward Jackson, Church Square (JDW)
Yates's Bar, Victoria Road (Yates)

Old Hartlepool ❯ Lighthouse

Seaton Carew ❯ Clock Tower (M&F) (Daytime)

MIDDLESBROUGH

Middlesbrough ❯ Bus Station
Hillstreet Shopping Centre (2) (Private)
The Mall Middlesbrough (Private)
Middlesbrough Station (Transpennine)
Debenhams Store, Newport Rd (Debenhams)
Isaac Walton, Wilson Street (JDW)
Nandos, North Ormsby Road (Nandos)
The Resolution, Newport Crescent (JDW)
The Shakespeare, Linthorpe Road (Walkabout)
Walkabout, Corporation Road (Private)
The Welly, Albert Road (M&B)
Yates's Bar, Newport Road (Yates)

North Ormesby ❯ Market Square
The Buccaneer, Kings Road (M&B)

NEWCASTLE UPON TYNE

Byker ❯ East End Library, Hadrian Sq (Library hrs)
East End Pool, Foyer (Pool hrs)
Shields Road/Edwin Street

Denton ❯ Denton Park Centre (Shopping hrs)

Fenham ❯ West Road Crematorium (Crematorium hrs)

Gosforth ❯ Scalini's, Great North Road (Private)

North East England

Kenton	❯	Kingston Park Stadium, East Stand (N'castle Falcons)
Newburn	❯	Newburn Country Park (9.00-22.00)
Newcastle upon Tyne	❯	Barrack Road, by St James Park (7.30-16.00)
		Chillingham Rd/Tosson Terrace
		Dean Street MSCP
		Eldon Gardens MSCP (8.00-22.00)
		Eldon Square, Sidgate (Trading hrs)
		Exhibition Park (7.30-21.00)
		Grainger Market (Market hrs)
		Haymarket, by Metro Station
		Newgate Street Car Park (Trading hrs)
		Paddy Freemans Park
		Percy Street Bus Concourse, Eldon Square
		Watergate, Quayside, by Swing Bridge
		The Gate Centre, Newgate Street (Private)
		Fenwicks Store, Northumberland Street (Private)
		Newcastle Station, Platform 4 (East Coast)
		Bar 38, Lombard St. (Private)
		Baron & Baroness, Times Square (Private)
		Centurion, Central Station (Private)
		Eye on the Tyne, Broad Chare (Private)
		Hide Bar, The Gate (Private)
		Job Bulman, St Nicholas Avenue (JDW)
		Keel Row, Newgate Street (JDW)
		Mile Castle, Westgate Rd/Grainger St (JDW)
		Mood, The Gate (Private)
		Nandos, Eldon Square (Nandos)
		Nandos, Newgate Street (Nandos)
		The Quayside, The Close (JDW)
		Revolution, Collingwood Street (Private)
		Union Rooms, Westgate Road (JDW)
		Waterline Bar, East Quayside (Private)
		The Yard, Scotswood Road (Private)
		Yates's Bar, Grainger Street (Yates)
		Metro Radio Arena, Arena Way (Private)
Woolsington	❯	Millers, Callerton Lane Ends (Private)

NORTH TYNESIDE

| Four Lane Ends | ❯ | Metro Interchange |
| Monkseaton | ❯ | Souter Park North |

Marden ❯ Fox Hunters, Prestongate (Private)

North Shields ❯ Duke Street
Fish Quay
Saville Street
Suez Street

Tynemouth ❯ Front Street
Long Sands North (May-Sept)
Tynemouth Park

Wallsend ❯ Forum Shopping Centre
Metro Bus Station
Gala Bingo, Middle Engine Lane (Gala)

Whitley Bay ❯ Central Lower Promenade (May-Sept)
Dukes Walk, Northern Promenade
Metro Station
Park Road, by Library
South Parade
Fire Station, York Road (JDW)
Old Hartley Caravan Club Site (Caravan Club)

NORTHUMBERLAND

Allendale ❯ Market Place

Alnmouth ❯ Alnmouth Station (Northern Rail)

Alnwick ❯ The Shambles

Amble ❯ Tourist Information Centre

Ashington ❯ Station Road (Daytime)
off Woodburn Road (Daytime)
Fox Cover, Newbiggin Road (Private)
Rohan Kanhai, Woodhorn Road (JDW)
Gala Bingo, Milburn Road (Gala)

Bamburgh ❯ Bamburgh Links Car Park
Church Street

Beadnell ❯ Car Park (Easter-October)

Bedlington ❯ Bower Grange, Station Road (Daytime)

Vulcan Place

Bellingham ❯ Main Street

Berwick-upon-Tweed ❯ Castlegate Car Park
Eastern Lane
Magdelene Fields
Woolmarket
Berwick Station, Platform 2 (East Coast)
Leaping Salmon, Golden Square (JDW)

Blyth ❯ Keel Row Shopping Centre
Market Place

Blyth Valley Links ❯ Fort House
Ranch Car Park

Boulmer ❯ Coastguard Cottage

Corbridge ❯ Princes Street

Cramlington ❯ Gala Bingo, Forum Way (Gala)

Craster ❯ Tourist Information Centre

East Ord ❯ Ord House Country Park (Private)

Etal ❯ Castle Car Park (Easter-October) (Pariash Council)

Haltwhistle ❯ Westgate

Heatherslaw Mill ❯ Car Park (M&F) (Easter-October) (Parish Council)

Hexham ❯ St Mary's Wynd
The Sele
Tyne Green
Wentworth Car Park
The Forum, Market Place (JDW)

Holy Island ❯ Green Lane Car Park

Housesteads ❯ Visitor Centre (National Trust)

Morpeth ❯ Back Riggs Bus Station (Town Council)
Carlisle Park (Town Council)
The Black Bull, Bridge Street (Private)

Newbiggin by the Sea ❯ Promenade, by "The Coble" (Daytime)

Norham ❯ off West Street (Parish Council)

Otterburn ❯ Main Street

Ponteland ❯ Thornhill Road Car Park (Daytime) (Town Council)

Powburn ❯ River Breamish Caravan Club Site (Caravan Club)

Prudhoe ❯ Neale Street
South Road

Riding Mill ❯ Wellington Hotel, Main Road (Private)

Seahouses ❯ Car Park

Seaton Sluice ❯ Fountainhead Bank Car Park (Daytime)
West Terrace Car Park

Spittal ❯ Promenade Car Park
Seaview Caravan Club Site (Caravan Club)

Wooler ❯ Bus Station

Wylam ❯ Main Road

REDCAR & CLEVELAND

Guisborough ❯ Fountain Street Car Park

Redcar ❯ Coatham Enclosure (April-September)
Esplanade West Terrace
Locke Park
Majuba Road Amusement Park (April-Sept)
Moore Street, off High Street
The Stray, opp. Green Lane (April-Sept)
Zetland Park, The Stray
Plimsoll Line, High Street East (JDW)
Royal Standard, West Dyke Road (Private)

Saltburn ❯ Cat Nab
Pier (Summer)

Upsall ❯ Cross Keys (Private)

SOUTH TYNESIDE

Hebburn ❯ Hebburn Shopping Centre (Mon-Sat)
The Longship, Usdaw Road (Private)

South Shields ❯ Coast Road, Marsden
Laygate Roundabout
Pier Parade (Daytime)
Promenade, Amusement Park (Summer)
Queen Street, by Metro Station
Sea Road
The Wouldhave, Mile End Road (JDW)
Yates's Bar, Mile End Road (Yates)

Whitburn ❯ Cornthwaite Park Car Park

STOCKTON-ON-TEES

Billingham ❯ Billingham Beck Country Park
Cowpen Bewley Woodland Park
Town Square

Eaglescliff ❯ Preston Park Country Park
Preston Park Museum (Museum hrs)

Stockton-on-Tees ❯ High Street
Ropner Park, Hartburn
Wellington Square Shopping Mall
Debenhams Store, High Street (Debenhams)
Thomas Sheraton, Bridge Road (JDW)

Tees Barrage ❯ White Water Caravan Club Site (Caravan Club)

Teesside Leisure Park ❯ Gala Bingo, Aintree Oval (Gala)

Thornaby ❯ Thornaby Station (Transpennine)

Yarm ❯ High Street

SUNDERLAND

Hetton ❯ Easington Lane, High Street
Town Centre Car Park, Front Street

Seaburn ❯ Seaburn Centre (Daytime)

South Bents (Summer)

Sunderland ❯ Harbour View, Roker Seafront
Lower Promenade, Roker Seafront
Park Lane Interchange
Park Parade, Roker (Daytime)
Southwick Green
Central Stores, Fawcett Street (Private)
Debenhams Store, The Bridges (Debenhams)
Bar Me, Low Row (Private)
Lampton Worm, Victoria Building (JDW)
Nandos, 118 High Street West (Nandos)
Old Orleans, Timber Beach Road (Private)
Varsity, Green Terrace (Barracuda)
William Jameson, Fawcett Street (JDW)
Yates's Bar, Burdon Road (Yates)
Gala Bingo, Pallion New Road (Gala)
Stadium of Light (Sunderland FC)

Washington ❯ Concord Centre, Bus Station
Sir William de Wessyngton (JDW)
Gala Bingo, The Galleries (Gala)

Scotland - South East

East Lothian

Athelstaneford	❯	Main Street (Summer, 9.00-21.00)
Dirleton	❯	Yellow Craig Caravan Club Site (Caravan Club)
Dunbar	❯	Bayswell Rd (10.00-17.00, later in Summer) Countess Crescent (9.00-18.00, later in Summer) John Muir Country Park (9.00-18.00, later in Summer) Shore Road (9.00-18.00, later in Summer) Skateraw (Summer, 9.00-21.00)
East Linton	❯	East Linton Park (9.00-18.00, later in Summer)
Haddington	❯	Neilson Park Rd. (9.00-18.00, later in Summer)
Longniddry	❯	Bents 2 (9.00-21.00 Summer & Winter weekends)
Musselburgh	❯	Shorthope Street (9.00-18.00, later in Summer) Fisherrow Harbour (9.00-18.00, later in Summer) CP
North Berwick	❯	Quality Street (9.00-18.00, later in Summer)
Port Seaton	❯	Links Rd. (9.00-20.00 Summer, 10-17.00 Winter)
Preston Pans	❯	Ayres Wynd (9.00-18.00, later in Summer)
Tranent	❯	Lindores Drive (9.00-18.00, later in Summer)

Edinburgh

Drumbrae South	❯	Rainbow Inn, Craigmount View (Private)
Edinburgh	❯	Ardmillan Terrace, Gorgie Road Bruntsfield Canonmills Castle Terrace Car Park (10.00-20.00) Hamilton Place (10.00-18.00) Haymarket, Morrison Street (M&F) (10.00-20.00) Hope Park (10.00-18.00) Joppa, Promenade

Mound, by Art Gallery
Nicolson Square (10.00-22.00)
Ross Band Stand, W Princes Street Gdns
(Summer, 8.00-20.00)
St James Centre (M&F) (10.00-18.00)
St John's Road (10.00-18.00)
Tollcross (10.00-20.00)
West End, W Princes Street Gdns (8.00-22.00)
Edinburgh Bus Station, Elder Street (Private)
Edinburgh Waverley Station (Network Rail)
Au Bar, Shandwick Place (Private)
Bar 38, George Street (Private)
Black Bull, Grassmarket (Private)
Browns, George Street (Private)
Edwards, South Charlotte Street (M&B)
Grape, Capital Building, St Andrews Sq (Private)
Hamiltons, Hamilton Place (Private)
Jongleurs, Omni Centre (Private)
McCowans Brew House", Fountain Park (Private)
Milnes Bar, Hanover Street (Private)
Nandos, Dundee Road, Fountain Park (Nandos)

National Key Scheme Toilets

Services for Communities are
responsible for Edinburgh's public
toilets and operate the National Key
Scheme in all our toilets with
disabled access.

Edinburgh has 31 public conveniences,
of which 18 have disabled access. For
a list of the locations of Edinburgh's
public conveniences please click on
http://www.edinburgh.gov.uk/internet/
City_Living/CEC_public_toilets.

For further information please contact:
0131 529 3030

·EDINBVRGH·
THE CITY OF EDINBURGH COUNCIL

SERVICE FOR COMMUNITIES

Playfair, Omni Centre (JDW)
Slug & Lettuce, Omni Centre (Private)
Standing Order, George Street (JDW)
Walkabout, Omni Centre (Private)
St Christophers Backpackers, Market St (Private)

Granton ⊙ Granton Square
Gala Bingo, West Granton Road (Gala)

Leith ⊙ Taylor Gardens, Gt. Junction Street
Foot of the Walk, Constitution Street (JDW)

Meadowbank ⊙ KFC Meadowbank (KFC)
Gala Bingo, Moray Park (Gala)

Morningside ⊙ Canaan Lane (10.00-18.00)

Newcraighall ⊙ Cuddie Brae, off City Bypass (Private)

Portobello ⊙ Bath Street (10.00-20.00)
Pipe Street

Silverknowles ⊙ Edinburgh Caravan Club Site (Caravan Club)

South Queensferry ⊙ High Street
Dalmeny Station (ScotRail)

Wester Hailes ⊙ Westside Plaza Shopping Centre (Private)
Gala Bingo, Westside Plaza (Gala)

FALKIRK

Blackness ⊙ The Square (9.00-17.00)

Bo'ness ⊙ Register Street Car Park
Kinneil Park, by Nursery (Park hrs)

Bonnybridge ⊙ High Street Car Park

Camelon ⊙ The Hedges, Main Street

Falkirk ⊙ Callendar Park (Park hrs)
Glebe Street (9.00-18.00)
Public Library, Hope Street (Library hrs)
Callendar Square Car Park (Private)

The Mall Howgate (2) (Private)
Falkirk Grahamston Station (ScotRail)
Falkirk High Station (ScotRail)
Carron Works, Bank Street (JDW)
Gala Bingo, Kerse Lane (Gala)

Grangemouth ❯ Earl of Zetland, Bo'ness Road (JDW)

Larbert ❯ Larbert Station (ScotRail)
Outside Inn, Glenbervie Business Pk (Private)

Polmont ❯ Polmont Station, Booking Hall (ScotRail)

MIDLOTHIAN

Dalkeith ❯ Blacksmiths Forge, Newmills Road (JDW)

Flotterstone Glen ❯ Visitor Centre, A707

SCOTTISH BORDERS

Broughton ❯ King George VI Park

Cockburnspath ❯ Main Street

Chirnside ❯ Cross Hill

Coldingham Sands ❯ Beach Front

Scottish Borders Council

For more information on Public Facilities and Access at many attractions, why not telephone for more details before you travel?

Please telephone
01835 825111 for all enquiries

Coldstream	❯	Courthouse
Duns	❯	Brierybaulk
Earlston	❯	Main Street
Eyemouth	❯	Harbour Road Car Park High Street Car Park
Galashiels	❯	Bank Street Bus Station High Street Car Park Hunters Hall, High Street (JDW)
Greenlaw	❯	The Square
Hawick	❯	Common Haugh Car Park, Victoria Road Howegate, Drumlanrig Square Volunteer Park
Innerleithen	❯	Hall Street
Jedburgh	❯	Lothian Car Park (7.30-18.00) Tourist Information Centre
Kelso	❯	Woodmarket/Horsemarket
Lauder	❯	Market Place
Melrose	❯	Abbey Street Gibson Park Caravan Club Site (Caravan Club)
Morebattle	❯	Main Street
Newcastleton	❯	Langholm Street, by Fire Station
Newton St Boswells	❯	Main Street
Peebles	❯	Eastgate Car Park Haylodge Park (Summer) Kingsmeadows Car Park School Brae, off High Street
St. Boswells	❯	Main Street

St Mary's Loch	❯	by Cafe
Selkirk	❯	Market Square Car Park
Town Yetholm	❯	off High Street
West Linton	❯	Main Street, opp. Graham Institute

WEST LOTHIAN

Bathgate	❯	James Young, Hopetoun Street (JDW)
Linlithgow	❯	Linlithgow Station (ScotRail)
Livingston	❯	McArthurGlen Designer Outlet (Private) Almond Bank, Almondvale Boulevard (JDW)

SCOTLAND - SOUTH WEST

DUMFRIES & GALLOWAY

Annan	❯	Downies Wynd
Ardwell	❯	Picnic site (Summer)
Balyett	❯	Picnic site (Summer)
Cairnryan	❯	Picnic site (Summer)
Carsthorn	❯	Shore Road
Castle Douglas	❯	Market Hill Car Park
Dalbeattie	❯	Water Street Car Park
Drummore	❯	Harbour Road
Dumfries	❯	Dock Park Munchies Street Whitesands Dumfries Station, Concourse (ScotRail) Robert the Bruce, Buccleuch Street (JDW) Gala Bingo, Shakespeare Street (Gala)
Gatehouse of Fleet	❯	High Street Car Park
Glenairle Bridge	❯	Picnic Site, A76
Glencaple	❯	Shore Road
Glenluce	❯	Public Hall, Main Street (Summer) Stairhaven (Summer)
Glentrool	❯	Stroan Bridge (Summer) Caldons Campsite (Forest Enterprise)
Gretna	❯	Kirtle Place (Daytime)
Kippford	❯	Village Hall Car Park
Kirkconnel	❯	Main Street (M&F) (Daytime)

Kirkcudbright	❯	Harbour Square
Langholm	❯	Kiln Green Car Park
Lockerbie	❯	Station Square Lockerbie Station (ScotRail)
Moffat	❯	Station Park
Moniave	❯	Ayr Road (M&F) (Daytime)
New Abbey	❯	Car Park
Newton Stewart	❯	Riverside Car Park Garlieston Caravan Club Site (Caravan Club)
Palnure	❯	Kirroughtree Visitor Centre (Forest Enterprise)
Penpont	❯	Marrburn Road Car Park (M&F) (Daytime)
Port Logan	❯	Fish Pond Car Park

	❯	New England Bay Caravan Club Site (Caravan Club)
Portpatrick	❯	Harbour
Port William	❯	Village Square
Sandhead	❯	Main Street
Sanquhar	❯	South Lochan (M&F) (Daytime)
Southerness	❯	Car Park, Shore Road
Stranraer	❯	Agnew Park Pavilion (Daytime) Hanover Square Car Park Sea Front Stair Park (Summer) Stranraer Station, Car Park (ScotRail)
Talnotry	❯	Talnotry Campsite (Forest Enterprise)
Thornhill	❯	St Cutherberts Walk (M&F) (Daytime)
Wanlockhead	❯	Lead Mining Museum (Summer)
Whithorn	❯	Bruce Street (Daytime)
Wigtown	❯	High Vennel

EAST AYRSHIRE

Cumnock	❯	Glaisnock Shopping Centre Cumnock Town Hall (Booking hrs)
Kilmarnock	❯	Burns Mall Shopping Centre Dick Institute Library & Gallery (Library hrs) Kilmarnock Station, Concourse (ScotRail) Wheatsheaf Inn, Portland Street (JDW) Gala Bingo, Portland Street (Gala)
Mauchline	❯	Loudoun Street

EAST DUNBARTONSHIRE

Bearsden ❯ Bearsden Cross

Bishopbriggs ❯ Eagle Lodge, Hilton Road (Private)

Clachan of Campsie ❯ Recreational Area

Kirkintilloch ❯ Southbank Road
Kirky Puffer, Townhead (Private)

Lenzie ❯ Lenzie Station (ScotRail)

Milngavie Mugdock Road
Cross Keys, Station Road (Private)
Milngavie station (ScotRail)

EAST RENFREWSHIRE

Barrhead ❯ Main Street

Busby ❯ White Cart, East Kilbride Road (Private)

Eaglesham ❯ Eaglesham Pavilion, Gilmour Street

Giffnock ❯ Rouken Glen Park, Car Park

Mearns ❯ The Avenue Shopping Centre (Private)

GLASGOW

Darnley ❯ Gala Bingo, Woodneuk Road (Gala)

Drumchapel ❯ Shopping Centre
Sainsbury's Store, Allerdyce Drive (Sainsbury)

Glasgow ❯ Buchanan Galleries (Private)
Princes Square, Buchanan St (Private)
St Enoch Shopping Centre (4) (Private)
Debenhams Store, Argyle St (Debenhams)
Buchanan Bus Station (2) (SPT)
Charing Cross Station (ScotRail)
Glasgow Central Station (Network Rail) (2)
Glasgow Queen Street Station (ScotRail)
All Bar One, St Vincent St (M&B)
The Arches, Argyle Street (Private)

Bar Censsa, West George Street (Private)
Barrachnie Inn, Glasgow Rd, Garrowhill (Private)
Buffalo Joes, Hope Street (Private)
Central Bar, Central Station (Private)
Counting House, St Vincents Place (JDW)
Crystal Palace, Jamaica Street (JDW)
Edward Wylie, Bothwell Street (JDW)
Edwards, West George Street (M&B)
Esquire House, Great Western Rd (JDW)
Frankenstein 1818, West George St (Private)
Hengler's Circus, Sauchihall Street (JDW)
Jongleurs, Renfrew Street (Private)
Mojama, Sauchiehall Street (Private)
Nandos, Glasgow Fort Shopping Centre (Nandos)
Nandos, The Quay, West Paisley Rd (Nandos)
Nandos, Silverburn Shopping Centre (Nandos)
O'Neills, Albion Street (M&B)
Sauciehaugh, Sauchiehall Street (Private)
Sir John Moore, Argyle Street (JDW)
Sir John Stirling Maxwell, Kilmarnock Rd (JDW)
Society Room, West George Street (JDW)
Walkabout, Renfield Street (Private)
Yates's Bar, Sauchiehall Street (Yates)
Yates's Bar, West George Street (Yates)
Carling Academy, Eglinton Street (Private)
Glasgow Bowl, Springfield Quay (AMF)
Scottish Exhibition & Conference Centre (Private)

Parkhead ❯ Forge Shopping Centre, Gallowgate (Private)

Partick ❯ Partick Interchange (SPT) [Planned]
Glasgow University Union (University)
Queen Margaret Union (University)

Possil Park ❯ Gala Bingo, Hawthorn Street (Gala)

INVERCLYDE

Gourock ❯ Albert Road (Daytime)
Shore Street (Daytime)
Gourock Station (ScotRail)

Greenock ❯ Campbell Street (Daytime)
Hunters Place
Kilblain Street (Daytime)
Greenock Central Station (ScotRail)

James Watt, Cathcart Street (JDW)

Inverkip ❯ Greenock Road (Daytime)

Port Glasgow ❯ Coronation Park (Daytime)
Port Glasgow Station (ScotRail)

Wemyss Bay ❯ Wemyss Bay Station (ScotRail)

NORTH AYRSHIRE

Ardrossan ❯ North Crescent Road (9.00-17.00)

Fairlie ❯ Main Road

Irvine ❯ East Road (9.00-18.00)
Low Green Road (9.00-14.00, later in Summer)
Shorehead (Summer Weekends, daytime)
Irvine Station (ScotRail)
Gala Bingo, Townhead (Gala)

Isle of Arran ❯ Blackwaterfoot, Harbour
Brodick, Public Green (Daytime in Winter)
Lamlash, Shore Road
Whiting Bay, Shore Road

Kilwinning ❯ Abbey Green
Kilwinning Station (ScotRail)

Largs ❯ Pierhead (Daytime)
Largs Station (ScotRail)

Saltcoats ❯ The Braes (9.30-20.00, later in Summer)
Melbourne Gardens (Apr-Sept 9.30-20.00)
The Salt Cot, Hamilton Street (JDW)

Stevenston ❯ Alexander Place/New Street
Stevenston Shore (Summer 12.00-18.00)

NORTH LANARKSHIRE

Airdrie ❯ Town Centre
Robert Hamilton, Bank Street (JDW)

Bellshill ❯ North Road
Avondale Bar/Lily Restaurant" (Private)

Coatbridge	❯	Main Street
		The Vulcan, Main Street (JDW)
Croy	❯	Croy Station, Ticket Office (ScotRail)
Cumbernauld	❯	Tay Walk (Shopping hrs) (Private)
		Teviot Walk (Shopping hrs) (Private)
		Tryst Sports Complex (CP)
		Cumbernauld Station (ScotRail)
Kilsyth	❯	King Street
Moodiesburn	❯	Pivot Community Education Centre (CP)
Motherwell	❯	Brandon Parade East
		Brandon Parade South
		Motherwell Station (ScotRail)
		Brandon Works, Merry Street (JDW)
Muirhead	❯	Muirhead Hotel (Private)
Shotts	❯	Town Centre
		Shotts Community Centre (CP)
Wishaw	❯	Kenilworth Avenue
		Wishaw Library (CP)
		Wishaw Malt, Kirk Road (JDW)

RENFREWSHIRE

Braehead	❯	Lord of the Isles, Xscape (JDW)
		Nandos, Xscape (Nandos)
		BowlPlex, Xscape (BowlPlex)
Paisley	❯	Paisley Gilmour Street Station (ScotRail)
		Last Post, County Square (JDW)
		Gala Bingo, Phoenix Retail Park (Gala)
Renfrew	❯	Inchinnan Road

SOUTH AYRSHIRE

Ayr	❯	Arthur Street
		Blackburn Car Park, Sea Front (Easter-Oct)
		Pavilion, Esplanade (M&F)

Ayr Station, Concourse (ScotRail)
West Kirk, Sandgate (JDW)
Craigie Gardens Caravan Club Site

Ballintrae ❯ Forelands

Girvan ❯ Ainslie Car Park
Flushes Car Park
Girvan Station (ScotRail)

Maidens ❯ Harbour

Prestwick ❯ Boydfield Gardens
Links Road (Summer & weekends in Winter)
(Private)
Prestwick Town Station (ScotRail)

Prestwick Airport ❯ Prestwick Airport Station (ScotRail)

Troon ❯ Church Street
St Meddans Street Car Park
Troon Station (ScotRail)

SOUTH LANARKSHIRE

Biggar ❯ Main Street (Daytime)

Carluke ❯ Carnwath Road (Daytime)

Carnwath ❯ Main Street

Carstairs ❯ Carstairs Station (ScotRail)

Crossford ❯ Lanark Road (Daytime)

East Kilbride ❯ Greenhills Shopping Centre
Maxwell Drive
Murray Owen Centre, Liddell Grove (CP)
Plaza Centre, Mall (Shopping hrs)
St Leonards Shopping Centre (8.00-20.00)
Peel Park, Eaglesham Road (Private)

Forth ❯ Main Street (Daytime)

Hamilton ❯ Bus Station, Brandon House (Daytime)

Kirkfieldbank ❯ Riverside Road

Lanark ❯ Horsemarket (Daytime)
Clydesdale Inn, Bloomgate (JDW)

Larkhall ❯ King Street

Law ❯ Station Road

Leadhills ❯ Main Street

Rutherglen ❯ Arcade
King Street
Community Leisure Centre, Glenside Drive (CP)

Stonehouse ❯ King Street

Strathaven ❯ Green Street

WEST DUNBARTONSHIRE

Alexandria ❯ Main StreetOvertoun Road
Leven Vale Pool (Pool hrs)

Balloch ❯ Old Balloch Station, by TIC

Clydebank ❯ The Playdrome, Abbotsford Road (Centre hrs) (CP)
Clyde Shopping Centre (Private)
In Shops, Syvania Road South (Private)
KFC, Livingstone Street (KFC)
Gala Bingo, Kilbowie Retail Park (Gala)

Dumbarton ❯ Riverside Lane (2)

SCOTLAND - EAST

ABERDEEN CITY

Aberdeen ❯ Central Library (Library hrs)
Skene Street/Summer Street
Stonehaven Road, A90 Lay-by
Debenhams Store, Trinity Centre (Debenhams)
Aberdeen Station, Concourse (ScotRail)
Archibald Simpson, Castle Street (JDW)
Beluga, Union Street (Private)
Cocket Hat, North Anderson Drive (Private)
J G Ross Coffee Shop, King St (Private)
Justice Mill, Union Street (JDW)
Nandos, Union Square (Nandos)
Slains Castle, Belmont Street (Private)
Yates's Bar, Langstane Place (Yates)
Gala Bingo, King Street (Gala)
Lynx Ice Centre (Centre hrs)

Cults ❯ North Deeside Road, by Library

Mastrick ❯ Sheddocksley Sports Centre (Centre hrs)

Peterculter ❯ North Deeside Road, by restaurant

ABERDEENSHIRE

Aberchider ❯ Market Street

Aboyne ❯ Ballater Road

Alford ❯ Car Park

Auchenblae ❯ Mackenzie Avenue

Auchnagatt ❯ Martin Terrace (Community Council)

Ballater ❯ The Square

Balmedie ❯ The Haughs (Summer, daytime)

Banchory ❯ Bellfield Car Park
Bridge of Feugh [Closed at present]
Silverbank Caravan Club Site (Caravan Club)

Banff	❯	Duff House Grounds St Mary's Car Park Harbour (June-Aug) (Community Council)
Bellabeg	❯	Strathdon
Bennachie	❯	Rowan Tree Car Park (April-October)
Boddam	❯	Harbour Street
Braemar	❯	Ballnellan Road Invercauld Caravan Club Site (Caravan Club)
Cornhill	❯	Mid Street
Crathie	❯	Car Park (April-October)
Crimond	❯	Logie Drive
Ellon	❯	Market Street
Fordyce	❯	East Church Street
Fraserburgh	❯	Castle Street Interpretive Centre Bus Station, Hanover Street (Private)
Fyvie	❯	Cummiestown Road

Aberdeenshire
COUNCIL

For more information on public facilities and access to many attractions, why not telephone for more details before you travel.

Please telephone for all enquiries:

08456 08 1207

Gardenstown	❯	The Harbour
Gourdon	❯	Boath Park
Hatton	❯	Station Road
Huntly	❯	Castle Street Market Muir
Insch	❯	Western Road
Inverallochy	❯	Allochy Road
Inverurie	❯	Station Road
Johnshaven	❯	Fore Street
Kintore	❯	Main Street/North Road
Maud	❯	Station Road
Mintlaw	❯	Aden Country Park, Coach House (Park hrs) Aden Country Park, Bottom Car Park (Summer) Aden Country Park Top Car Park (Summer) The Square
New Byth	❯	Playing Fields
New Pitsligo	❯	High Street/Market Place
Oldmeldrum	❯	Urquhart Road
Peterhead	❯	Drummers Corner/Tolbooth Cross Keys, Back Street (JDW) Gala Bingo, Marischal Street (Gala)
Port Elphinstone	❯	Port Road
Portsoy	❯	Shore Street
Potarch	❯	Potarch Green
Rosehearty	❯	Union Street
Stonehaven	❯	Harbour Margaret Street

Scotland - East

Strichen	❯	Bridge Street
Stuartfield	❯	Knock Field (April-October)
Tarves	❯	Pleasure Park, Tolquhon Avenue
Turriff	❯	High Street
Westhill	❯	Shopping Centre Shepherds Rest, Arnhall Business Pk. (Private)
Woods of Logie	❯	-

ANGUS

Arbroath	❯	Hamilton Green Harbour Visitor Centre Market Place Ness-Victoria Park Tennis Courts (April-October) Arbroath Station (ScotRail) Corn Exchange, Market Place (JDW) Gala Bingo, High Street (Gala)
Auchmithie	❯	Fountain Square
Brechin	❯	Church Street
Edzell	❯	The Muir

Forfar	❯	Buttermarket
Monifieth	❯	Riverview Drive, Play Area (April-Sept)
Montrose	❯	Trail Pavilion Town Buildings Montrose Station (ScotRail) Gala Bingo, Hume Street (Gala)

DUNDEE

Broughty Ferry	❯	Beach, Windmill Gardens (9.00-18.00) CP Queen Street Car Park Bell Tree, Panmurefield Road (Private)
Dundee	❯	Hilltown McManus Galleries (Museum hrs) Seagate Bus Station (Daytime) Tayside House (Office hrs) Wellgate Library (Library hrs) Debenhams Store, Overgate (Debenhams) Dundee Station (ScotRail) The Capitol, Seagate (JDW) Counting House, Reform Street (JDW) Outside Inn, Camperdown Park (Private) Yates's Bar, Seagate (Yates) Gala Bingo, The Stack Leisure Park (Gala) Pamis, Springfield House, Dundee University (Private) (CP)
Lochee	❯	Aimer Square Car Park

FIFE

Aberdour	❯	Aberdour Station (ScotRail)
Burntisland	❯	Links Place (8.30-19.00, later in Summer)
Cowdenbeath	❯	Cowdenbeath Station (ScotRail)
Cupar	❯	Bonnygate Car Park Cupar Station (ScotRail)
Dunfermline		Dunfermline Town Station (ScotRail) Nandos, Fife Leisure Park (Nandos) Bowlplex, Fife Leisure Park (Bowlplex)

Dysart	❯	Harbour (April-November)
Glenrothes	❯	Church Street Bus Station (opening hrs) Glamis Centre Kingdom Shopping Centre (2) Golden Acorn, North Street (JDW)
Inverkeithing	❯	Inverkeithing Station (ScotRail) Burgh Arms, High Street (Private)
Kinghorn	❯	Kinghorn Station (ScotRail)
Kingsbarns	❯	The Beach (April-September, 7.00-20.00)
Kirkcaldy		Esplanade (8.30-19.00) Beverage Park (Park hrs) Bus Station (opening hrs) Ravenscraig Park (Park hrs) Kirkcaldy Station (ScotRail) William Hill, Dunearn Drive (Private) Robert Nairn, Kirk Wynd (JDW)
Leuchars	❯	Leuchars Station (ScotRail)
Leven	❯	Bus Station, Branch Street Promenade (10.00-16.00, later in Summer) Gala Bingo, Commercial Road (Gala)
Markinch	❯	Markinch Station (Scotrail) Balbirnie Park Caravan Club Site (Caravan Club)
Newport	❯	Blyth Hall
Pittenweem	❯	The Harbour (Daytime)
St Andrews	❯	Bruce Embankment (Daytime) Bus Station, City Road Church Square (8.00-20.00)
St Monans	❯	Hope Place (Daytime)
Tayport	❯	The Harbour

PERTH & KINROSS

Auchterarder ❯ Crown Wynd Car Park

Blair Atholl ❯ Village Hall Car Park

Blairgowrie ❯ Wellmeadow

Comrie ❯ Dalginross

Crieff ❯ James Square

Dunkeld ❯ North Car Park

Perth ❯ Bus Station, Leonard Street
Marshall Place (8.00-18.00)
Ropemakers Close (8.30-18.00)
St Johns Shopping Centre (Private)
Perth Station, Entrance Hall (ScotRail)
Capital Asset, Tay Street (JDW)

Pitlochry ❯ West Lane (9.00-18.00)
Pitlochry Station (ScotRail)

St Fillans ❯ Main Street

Turfhills   M90 ❯ Kinross Services, J6 M90 (Moto)

STIRLING

Callander	❯	South Church Street Station Road
Crianlarich	❯	Glenfalloch Road
Dunblane	❯	Dunblane Station, Platform 1 (ScotRail)
Killin	❯	Maragowan Caravan Club Site (Caravan Club)
Stirling	❯	Bus Station (Private) Stirling Station, Platform 2 (ScotRail) Debenhams Store, Thistle Centre (Debenhams) Nandos, Forthside (Nandos) Stirling Bowl, Forth Street (AMF)

SCOTLAND - HIGHLANDS & ISLANDS

ARGYLL & BUTE

Ardrishaig ❯ Car Park (8.00-17.00, later in Summer)

Campbeltown ❯ Bolgam Street, off Main Street (8.00-18.00)
Pensioners Row (9.30-17.00)

Dunoon ❯ Glenmorag, West Bay (Summer, 8.00-20.00)
Moir Street (8.00-22.00)

Helensburgh ❯ Kidston Park, The Pier (9.00-14.00, later in Summer)

Innellan ❯ Shore Road, Sandy Beach (Summer)

Inveraray ❯ The Pier (7.00-20.30, later in Summer)

Isle of Bute ❯ Ettrick Bay (April-Sept 10.00-19.00)
Port Bannatyne
Rothsey Pier

Isle of Gigha ❯ -

Isle of Islay ❯ Port Ellen, Charlotte Street
Portnahaven

Isle of Mull ❯ Craignure
Fionnphort
Tobermory (Harbour Assn)

Kilcreggan ❯ Pier (9.00-16.00, later in Summer)

Killegruer ❯ Glenbarr Caravan Site

Kilmun ❯ The Pier

Lochgilphead ❯ Lochnell St (7,00-17.00, later in Summer)

Loch Lomond ❯ Firkin Point (8.00-16.00, later in Summer)

Luss ❯ Car Park (8.00-16.00, later in Summer)

Oban ❯ Oban Station (ScotRail)

Rhu	❯	Main Road (9.00-16.00, later in Summer)
Sandbank	❯	Main Road (8.00-20.00)
Tarbert	❯	Harbour Street (7.00-18.00, later in Summer)
Taynuilt	❯	School Road

HIGHLAND

Achiltibuie	❯	North of Village
Achnasheen	❯	Achnasheen Station (ScotRail)
Applecross	❯	Shore Street
Arisaig	❯	by village shop
Ardgay	❯	(Summer only)
Aviemore	❯	Main Street
Beauly	❯	High Street (M&F)
Bettyhill	❯	Car Park, A836
Bonar Bridge	❯	Picnic Site
Brora	❯	Dalcham Caravan Club Site (Caravan Club)
Carrbridge	❯	Car Park
Clachtoll	❯	Beach
Corran	❯	by Ferry
Cromarty	❯	Allan Square
Culloden	❯	Culloden Moor Caravan Club Site (Caravan Club)
Daviot Wood	❯	A9 Northbound, by Information Centre
Dingwall	❯	Tulloch Street

Dores	⊘	Dores Inn
Drumbeg	⊘	Car Park
Drumnadrochit	⊘	Tourist Information Centre Car Park
Dunbeath	⊘	Harbour
Dunnet Bay	⊘	Beach
Fort Augustus	⊘	A82, by Tourist Information Centre
Fort William	⊘	Viewforth Car Park Fort William Station (ScotRail)
Gairloch	⊘	Community Centre (M&F) (Centre hrs) Harbour Road
Golspie	⊘	Car Park off Main Street
Glencoe	⊘	Car Park opp. hotel
Grantown	⊘	High Street (April-Oct) Burnfield
Invergordon	⊘	King Street
Invermoriston	⊘	Glenmoriston Millennium Hall
Inverness	⊘	Castle Wynd Mealmarket Close Inverness Station (ScotRail) The Fluke, Culcabock Road (Private) Kings Highway, Church Street (JDW)
Isle of Skye	⊘	Ardvasar, Village Hall Broadford, opp. Visitor Car Park Carbost, opp. The Distillery Dunvegan, Visitor Car Park Kilmuir, by Thatched Museum Portree, Camanachd Square Portree, The Green Uig, Visitor Car Park
John O'Groats	⊘	Car Park

Keiss	>	Main Street
Kinlochewe	>	Slioch Terrace Kinlochewe Caravan Club Site (Caravan Club)
Kinlochleven	>	nr. Ice Factor
Kyle of Lochalsh	>	Car Park Kyle of Lochalsh Station (ScotRail)
Lairg	>	Main Street
Lochcarron	>	by Village Hall
Lochinver	>	Main Street
Mallaig	>	East Bay Car Park Mallaig Station (ScotRail)
Muir of Ord	>	Seaforth Road
Nairn	>	Court House Lane East Beach, Car Park Harbour Street The Links, West Beach Mill Road
North Kessock	>	Picnic Area, A9 Northbound (Daytime) Picnic Area, A9 Southbound (Daytime)
Onich	>	Bunree Caravan Club Site (Caravan Club)
Portmahomack	>	Main Street (April-October)
Rogie Falls	>	Car Park, A835 (April-October)
Rosemarkie	>	Mill Road
Shiel Bridge	>	Morvich Caravan Club Site (Caravan Club)
Silver Bridge	>	Car Park, A835
Smoo	>	Smoo Cave
Strathpeffer	>	The Square (April-October)

Tain	❯	Rose Garden, off High Street (2)
Tarbet, Sutherland	❯	Tarbet Pier
Thurso	❯	Harbour Tanyard, Riverside Road
Ullapool	❯	West Argyle Street (M&F)
Wick	❯	Whitechapel Road Wick Station (ScotRail) Alexander Blain, Market Place (JDW)

MORAY

Aberlour	❯	Alice Littler Park (8.00-16.00, later in Summer)
Buckie	❯	Fish Market (8.00-16.00, later in Summer) Newlands Lane Car Park (8.00-17.00, later in Summer)
Burghhead	❯	Harbour (8.00-16.00, later in Summer)
Craigellachie	❯	Victoria Road, A95 (Community Council)
Cullen	❯	Cullen Harbour (April-October 8.00-20.00) The Square (8.00-16.00, later in Summer)
Dufftown	❯	Albert Place Car Park (8.00-16.00, later in Summer)
Elgin	❯	Elgin Library (Library hrs) Cooper Park (April-Oct, 8.00-20.00) Elgin Station (ScotRail) Tesco Store, Lossie Green (Tesco) Muckle Cross, High Street (JDW)
Findhorn	❯	The Beach, Middle Block (M&F) The Beach, West Block (M&F)
Findochty	❯	Edindoune Shore (8.00-16.00, later in Summer)
Forres	❯	Grant Park (April-Oct, 8.00-20.00) The Leys (9.00-17.00, later in Summer) Forres Station (ScotRail)

Garmouth	◉	Playing Field (April-October)
Hopeman	◉	Harbour (8.00-16.00, later in Summer)
Keith	◉	Regent Square (8.00-16.00, later in Summer) Reidhaven (8.00-16.00, later in Summer) (M&F) Keith Station (ScotRail)
Lossiemouth	◉	Esplanade (8.00-16.00, later in Summer) (M&F) Station Park (8.00-16.00, later in Summer)
Portknockie	◉	Harbour (April-Oct, 8.00-20.00)
Rothes	◉	New Street (8.00-16.00, later in Summer) (M&F)
Tomintoul	◉	Back Lane (8.00-16.00, later in Summer)

ORKNEY ISLANDS

Deerness	◉	Community Hall (Community Council)
Evie	◉	Aikerness Tingwall Pier Waiting Room
Finstown	◉	Maitland Place
Kirkwall	◉	Peedie Sea Boat Store, Pickaquoy Road St Magnus Lane, off Broad Street (Daytime) Shapinsay Ferry Terminal (Terminal hrs) Shore Street Scapa Beach Kirkwall Travel Centre (CP)
Orphir	◉	Waulkmill
Sanday	◉	Kettletoft Pier Waiting Room
Sandwick	◉	Bay of Skaill
South Ronaldsay	◉	Sands O'Wright 4th Barrier
Stromness	◉	Ferry Road Warbeth Beach

| Stronsay | ⊗ | Whitehall Pier |

SHETLAND ISLANDS

| Lerwick | ⊗ | Harbour House
The Viking Bus Station |

| Scalloway | ⊗ | Burn Beach Car Park (8.00-21.00) |

WESTERN ISLES

| Stornoway | ⊗ | Percival Square, opp. Tourist Information Centre |

WALES - NORTH

ISLE OF ANGLESEY

Aberffraw ❯ Llys Llywelyn (Summer)

Amlwch ❯ Lon Goch

Beaumaris ❯ by Library

Benllech ❯ Beach Car Park (Summer)
Square Car Park

Brynsiencyn ❯ Car Park (Summer)

Cemaes ❯ Beach Car Park
High Street

Church Bay ❯ Beach Car Park (Summer)

Holyhead ❯ Breakwater Park (Summer)
Newry Beach
Porth Dafarch (Summer)
South Stack (Summer)
Swift Square
Holyhead Ferry Terminal (Stena)

Llanddona ❯ Beach (Summer)

Llaneilian ❯ Beach (Summer)

Llanfairpwll ❯ Car Park, by Post Office

Llangefni ❯ Lon y Felin

Llannerch-y-Medd ❯ High Street

Menai Bridge ❯ Bowling Green/Beach Road (Summer)
Library
Pier

Newborough ❯ Beach Road Car Park (Summer)

Penrhos ❯ Nature Reserve Beach (Summer)
Penrhos Caravan Club Site (Caravan Club)

Red Wharf Bay	❯	(Summer)
Rhoscolyn	❯	Beach Car Park (Summer)
Rhosneigr	❯	Library Car Park
Traeth Bychan	❯	Car Park (Summer)
Trearddur Bay	❯	Beach Car Park (Summer)
Valley	❯	Council Car Park

CONWY

Abergele	❯	Beefield, Car Park Water Street
Betwys-y-Coed	❯	Pont-y-Pair Car Park Station Road Car Park
Cerrigydrudion	❯	Tan Llan, off A55
Colwyn Bay	❯	The Close Douglas Road Car Park Eiras Park Eiras Park Coach Park Ivy Street Lansdowne Road Car Park Promenade, Central Promenade, Dingle (April-September) Colwyn Bay Station (Arriva Wales) Picture House, Princes Drive (JDW)
Conwy	❯	Bodlondeb (April-September) Morfa Bach Car Park (April-September) The Quay Castle Visitor Centre (Cadw)
Deganwy	❯	Level Crossing
Dolwyddelan	❯	by Post Office
Kinmel Bay	❯	The Square, Foryd Road
Llanddulas	❯	Station Road (April-September)

Llandudno	⊘	George Street
		Great Orme Visitor Centre (April-September)
		Happy Valley Road
		Llanrhos Cemetery
		Mostyn Broadway Coach Park
		North Shore, nr. Paddling Pool
		Llandudno Station (Arriva Wales)
		Dale Park Café, West Shore (Private)
		The Palladium, Gloddaeth Street (JDW)
Llandudno Junction	⊘	Osborne Road Car Park, off A55
		Llandudno Junction Station (Arriva Wales) [2010]
Llanelian	⊘	by Recreation Field (April-September)
Llanfair Talhaearn	⊘	School Lane, off A548
Llanfairfechan	⊘	Promenade, Car Park
		Rhandir Cemetery
Llanrwst	⊘	Gwydyr Park (April-September)
		Plas-yn-Dre
		Watling Street
Llansannan	⊘	Canol y Llan
Penmaenmawr	⊘	Fernbrook Road Car Park, off A55
		Promenade by Subway (April-September)
		Promenade, West End (April-September)
		Station Road Car Park
Pentrefoelas	⊘	Monument, off A55
Rhos-on-Sea	⊘	Cayley Promenade
		Marine Drive (April-September)
Towyn	⊘	Sandbank Road
Trefriw	⊘	Gower Road

DENBIGHSHIRE

Corwen	⊘	Rug Chapel (CADW)
Denbigh	⊘	Rosemary Lane

Llangollen	❯	Market Street
Loggerheads	❯	Country Park (Park hrs)
Prestatyn	❯	Barkby Beach Bus Station, Ffordd Pendyffryn Council Offices, Nant Hall Road (Office hrs) The Nova, Central Beach
Rhuddlan	❯	Princes Road (dawn-dusk)
Rhyl	❯	Coromation Gardens (Park hrs) Events Arena Old Golf Road Railway Station (Daytime) Town Hall West Parade, Childrens Village Rhyl Station (Arriva Wales) [2009/10] Sussex, Sussex Street (JDW)
Ruthin	❯	Market Street
St Asaph	❯	High Street, nr. Bridge (Daytime)

FLINTSHIRE

Caerwys	❯	Drovers Lane
Cilcain	❯	Village Community Centre
Connah's Quay	❯	Fron Road
Flint	❯	Flint Station (Arriva Wales)
Holywell	❯	Somerfield Car Park Tower Gardens Car Park
Mold	❯	Bus Station Daniel Owen Centre (Mon-Sat 8.00-18.00) New Street Car Park Gold Cape, Wrexham Street (JDW)
Saltney	❯	High Street
Shotton	❯	Alexander Street

GWYNEDD

Aberdaron ❯ The Beach (Daytime)

Aberdyfi ❯ The Quay

Abersoch ❯ Golf Road (April-October)
The Harbour (Daytime)

Bala ❯ The Green
Plassey Street

Bangor ❯ Glanrafon (Daytime)
Tan y Fynwent (Daytime)
Bangor Station (Arriva Wales)
Black Bull Inn, High Street (JDW)
Varsity, High Street (Barracuda)

Barmouth/Abermaw ❯ Llys Cambrian, nr Station (Daytime)
The Quay (Daytime)
North Promenade (Apr-Oct, Daytime)

Beddgelert ❯ Village
Ty Isaf (National Trust)

Blaenau Ffestiniog ❯ Diffwys
Coed-y-Llwyn Caravan Club Site
(Caravan Club)

Caernarfon ❯ Castle Hill (Daytime)
by Empire (Daytime)
Penllyn Car Park (Daytime)
Tafarn y Porth, Eastgate Street (JDW)

Criccieth ❯ Car Park (Daytime)
Esplanade (April-Oct, Daytime)
Marine (April-Oct, Daytime)
Criccieth Castle (CADW)

Dinas Dinlle ❯ by The Marine (Daytime)
Y Morfa Goch (Summer, Daytime)

Dolgellau ❯ Marian Mawr Car Park

Fairbourne/Y Friog ❯ Penrhyn Drive South

Harlech	❯	Bron y Graig by Castle (April-September)
Llanberis	❯	Ger y Llyn (Daytime) Maes Padarn (Daytime) Y Glyn (M&F) (April-Sept, Daytime)
Llandanwg	❯	The Beach
Llithfaen	❯	Village
Machroes	❯	by Beach (April-Oct, Daytime)
Maentwrog	❯	by Oakeley Arms
Morfa Bychan	❯	Beach Entrance (Apr-Oct)
Mynytho	❯	Chwarel Foel Gron (May-September)
Nefyn	❯	Cefn Twr (Daytime)
Penrhyndeudraeth	❯	Car Park (Daytime)
Porthmadog	❯	Public Park (Daytime)
Pwllheli	❯	Penlan (Daytime) South Beach (Daytime) Y Maes/The Square (Daytime) West End (Daytime)
Trawsfynydd	❯	Car Park
Trefor	❯	Y Traeth (May-Sept, Daytime)
Tudweiliog	❯	Village (Apr-Oct)
Tywyn	❯	by Cinema Recreation Ground
Y Felinheli	❯	Beach Road (Daytime)

WREXHAM

Cefn-Mawr	❯	Ty-Maer Country Park (Park hrs)

Chirk	❯	Colliery Road Car Park
		Lady Margaret's Park Caravan Club Site (Caravan Club)
Coedpoeth	❯	High Street Car Park
Erddig	❯	Country Park (National Trust)
Froncysyllte	❯	A5
Holt	❯	Cross Street (Community Council)
Overton	❯	School Street Car Park (Community Council)
Rhosllanerchrugog	❯	Market Street
Rossett	❯	The Green, Chester Road (Community Council)
Trevor	❯	Canal Basin Car Park
Wrexham	❯	Henblas Street

Wrexham

Henblas Street
St Giles Link Road
Waterworld Car Park
Wrexham General Station (Arriva Wales)
Elihu Yale, Regent Street (JDW)
Nandos, Eagles Meadow (Nandos)
North & South Wales Bank, High Street (JDW)
Yates's Bar, High Street (Yates)

WALES- MID & WEST

CARMARTHENSHIRE

Abergorlech ❯ Village Centre

Alltwalis ❯ Village Centre (8.00-18.00)

Ammanford ❯ Bus Station Car Park (9.00-18.00, later in Summer)
Carregamman Car Park (6.00-20.00)

Brechfa ❯ Village

Burry Port ❯ Harbour (8.00-18.00)
by Railway Station (7.30-17.00, later in Summer)

Carmarthen ❯ Carmarthen Market
John Street Car Park (6.00-20.00)
St Peters Car Park (6.00-20.00)
Carmarthen Bus Station (Private)
Carmarthen Station, Platform 1 (Arriva Wales)
Yr Hen Dderwen, King Street (JDW)

Carreg Cennen ❯ Castle Car Park

Cenarth ❯ Village (9.00-18.00)

Cross Hands ❯ Bristol House, off end of M4
Carmarthen Road, nr. Square (8.30-16.00)

Cynwyl Elfed ❯ Village (7.30-17.30)

Ferryside ❯ Village (7.30-19.00, later in Summer)

Glanamman ❯ Cwmamman Square (9.00-18.00, later in Summer)

Gorslas ❯ Car Park (7.30-20.00)

Kidwelly ❯ Square (7.30-17.00, later in Summer)
Kidwelly Castle (CADW)

Laugharne ❯ below Castle (6.00-20.00)

Llanboidy ❯ Village (8.00-17.00, later in Summer))

Llanddowror	❯	by Church (7.30-17.00, later in Summer)
Llandeilo	❯	Crescent Road Car Park (6.00-20.00)
Llandovery	❯	Castle Car Park (6.00-20.00, later in Summer)
Llanelli	❯	Island Place Bus Station (6.00-20.00) Provision Market (Mon-Sat 8.00-17.30) Parc Howard (Park hrs) Town Hall Square0 (6.00-20.00) North Dock Beach (Millennium Coastal Park) Llanelli Station (Arriva Wales) [2009/10] York Palace, Stepney Street (JDW) Pembrey Country Park Caravan Club Site (Caravan Club)
Llanpumsaint	❯	Village (8.00-16.30, later in Summer)
Llansaint	❯	Welfare Hall (8.00-18.00)
Llansteffan	❯	Car Park, South (8.00-17.30, later in Summer) Green (Apr-Oct, 8.00-21.00)
Llanybydder	❯	by Cross Hands hotel (07.00-19.00) Car Park (5.00-18.30)
Llyn Llech Owain	❯	Country Park (Park hrs)
Meidrim	❯	Village Centre (7.00-17.00, later in Summer)
Meinciau	❯	Community Hall (8.00-17.30)
Newcastle Emlyn	❯	Cattle Mart (8.30-18.00, later in Summer)) Cawdor Buildings
Pencader	❯	Village (7.30-17.30)
Pendine	❯	Car Park (7.30-18.00, later in Summer) Spring Well (Apr-Oct, 7.30-22.00)
Pontwelli	❯	by Wilkes Head (8.00-18.00)
St Clears	❯	Car Park (6.00-22.00)

Talley	❯	nr. Abbey
Tumble	❯	High Street (8.30-16.00)
Velindre	❯	Parc Puw (8.00-20.00)
Whitland	❯	Cross Street (8.00-18.00, later in Summer)

CEREDIGION

Aberaeron	❯	Masons Road North Beach Pen Cei
Aberporth	❯	Glanmardy Penrodyn
Aberystwyth	❯	Bath Street Castle Grounds Harbour Marine Terrace, The Shelter Park Avenue Aberystwyth Station, Platform 1 (Arriva Wales) Varsity, Upper Portland St (Barracuda) Yr Hen Orsaf, Alexandra Road (JDW) Glan-y-Mor Leisure Park (Private)

Borth	❯	by Coastguard, South Beach Pantyfedwyn, North Beach Swn-y-Mor Leisure Park (Private)
Cardigan/Aberteifi	❯	Bath House Greenfield Car Park Victoria Gardens
Cenarth	❯	Town
Devils Bridge	❯	behind Village Shop
Lampeter	❯	Market Street Car Park Rookery Lane Car Park St Thomas Street
Llanarth	❯	Shawsmead Caravan Club Site (Caravan Club)
Llandysul	❯	Car Park
Llangrannog	❯	Ger y Traeth/Beachside
Llanrhystud	❯	Pengarreg Caravan Park (Private)
New Quay/Cei Newydd	❯	Paragon Car Park South John Street
Penbryn	❯	Penbryn Beach
Tregaron	❯	Car Park
Tresaith	❯	Ger y Traeth/Beachside

PEMBROKESHIRE

Amroth	❯	Amroth West
Bosherston	❯	Car Park
Broad Haven	❯	Marine Road National Park Car Park (April-October)
Burton	❯	Jolly Sailor Car Park (April-October)
Carew	❯	opp. The Castle

Cilgerran	❯	Picnic Site
Cresswell Quay	❯	Quay
Crymych	❯	Main Road, The Square
Dale	❯	Coronation Hall
Dinas Cross	❯	A487 Main Road by Playing Field
Felindre Farchog	❯	A487 Lay-by
Fishguard	❯	The Square (Daytime) West Street Car Park (Daytime) Fishguard Ferry Terminal (Stena)
Freshwater	❯	East West Freshwater East Caravan Club Site (Caravan Club)
Goodwick	❯	Parrog Car Park
Gwaun Valley	❯	-
Haverfordwest	❯	Castle Lake (Daytime) Riverside MSCP (Daytime) Leisure Centre (Daytime)
Johnston	❯	Pope Hill
Kilgetty	❯	Tourist Information Car Park
Letterston	❯	The Square
Little Haven	❯	Car Park
Manorbier	❯	Beach
Marloes	❯	-
Milford Haven	❯	Gelliswick Manchester Square (Daytime) Market Square (Daytime) The Rath (Daytime)

Moylegrove	❯	-
Narberth	❯	Towns Moor Car Park (Daytime)
Nevern	❯	behind Old School
Newgale	❯	Central Car Park By Duke of Edinburgh (April-October)
Newport	❯	Long Street Car Park
Neyland	❯	Brunel Quay Marina
Nolton Haven	❯	- (Summer)
Pembroke	❯	Commons (Daytime) Parade
Pembroke Dock	❯	Front Street Hobbs Point (Daytime) Library (Daytime)
Penally	❯	-
Penblewin	❯	Car Park
Porthgain	❯	-
St Davids	❯	Bryn Road, behind City Hall The Grove Car Park (Daytime, April-Oct) Porthclais Quickwell Hill Car Park Whitesands Beach Car Park Lleithyr Meadow Caravan Club Site (Caravan Club)
St Dogmaels	❯	High Street Poppit Sands
St Florence	❯	Village Hall (Hall Committee)
St Ishmaels	❯	- (April-October)
St Nicholas	❯	Village Hall, nr. Church (Hall Committee)

Saundersfoot ❯ Coppit Hall Car Park (Daytime, April-Oct)
Harbour Car Park (Daytime)
Regency Car Park (Daytime, April-Oct)

Solva ❯ Lower Car Park

Stackpole ❯ Stackpole Quay (National Trust)

Stepaside ❯ Heritage Centre (April-Oct)

Templeton ❯ Play Area (April-October)

Tenby ❯ Buttsfield Car Park (Daytime)
Castle Beach (Daytime)
MSCP (Daytime)
North Beach
Salterns Car Park
South Beach (Daytime, Summer)
Upper Frog Street

Trevine ❯ -

Wisemans Bridge ❯ -

POWYS

Abergwesyn ❯ Community Hall (Summer) (Community Council)

Powys

Gwasanaethau Adfywio
a'r Amgylchedd

www.powys.gov.uk
0845 607 6060

Brecon	❯	Lion Yard
		Produce Market (Market Days)
		Promenade, Upper Meadow
		Theatr Brycheiniog
		Brynich Caravan Park (Private)
Builth Wells	❯	Groe Car Park
		The Strand (Town Council)
Caersws	❯	Bridge Street
Carno	❯	nr. Post Office
Clywedog	❯	Y Dremfadeg, Main Dam (Severn Trent)
Crickhowell	❯	Beaufort Street (Private)
Glasbury-on-Wye	❯	off A438
Hay-on-Wye	❯	Oxford Road Car Park
Knighton	❯	Norton Arms Car Park
		Offa's Dyke Centre (Daytime)
Lake Vyrnwy	❯	by Main Dam & Estate Office (Severn Trent)
Llananno	❯	A483, between Crossgates & Newtown
Llanbrynmair	❯	Car Park
Llandrindod Wells	❯	Lakeside (Daytime)
		Station Crescent
		Town Hall Grounds
		The Metropole, Temple Street (Private)
Llanfair Caereinion	❯	Bridge Street
Llanfihangell-yng-Ngwynfa		Car Park (Community Council)
Llanfyllin	❯	High Street, opp. Car Park
Llangorse Common	❯	Car Park
Llangynog	❯	Car Park

Llanidloes	❯	Gro Car Park
Llanrhaeadr-ym-Mochnant		Village
		Waterfall
Llansantffraed		A40, west of Bwlch
Llansanffraidd	❯	A495 Main Road
Llanspyddid	❯	A40, west of Brecon
Llanwrtyd Wells	❯	nr. New Inn
Machynlleth	❯	Maengwyn Street Car Park
		Machynlleth Station (Arriva Wales) [2010]
Meifod	❯	Car Park
Newtown	❯	Back Lane Car Park
		Gravel Car Park
Pen-y-Cae	❯	Craig-y-Nos Country Pk (Brecon Beacons NP)
Presteigne	❯	Hereford Street
		Wilson Terrace (Daytime) (Town Council)
Rhayader	❯	Dark Lane
Sennybridge	❯	High Street
Storey Arms	❯	A470, between Brecon & Merthyr
Talgarth	❯	The Square
Tretower	❯	Tretower Court & Castle (CADW)
Welshpool	❯	Berriew Street Car Park
		Church Street Car Park
Ystradfellte	❯	Porth-yr-Ogof Car Park (Brecon Beacons NP)
Ystrydgynlais	❯	The Cross

Wales - Mid & West

WALES - SOUTH

BLAENAU GWENT

Abertillery	❯	Tillery Street

Blaina	❯	Blaina Cemetery (Daytime) Cwm Celyn Road

Cwm	❯	Cwm Cemetery (Daytime)

Brynmawr	❯	Brynmawr Cemetery (Daytime) Market Square

Ebbw Vale	❯	Ebbw Vale Cemetery (Daytime) Market Street Picture House, Market Street (JDW)

Tredegar	❯	Cefn Golau Cemetery (Daytime) Dukestown Cemetery (Daytime) Gwent Shopping Centre (Private) Olympia, Morgan Street (JDW)

BRIDGEND

Bridgend	❯	Brackla Street, Cheapside Bridgend Bus Station Bridgend Station, Platform 1 (Arriva Wales) Dunraven Arms, Derwen Road (Private) Ikon Nightclub, Nolton Street (Private) Lava Lounge, Nolton Street (Private) Litten Tree, opp. Bus Station (Private) O'Neils, Nolton Street (Private) Tuskers Bar, Wyndham Street (Private) West House, Cefn Glas (Private) Wyndham Arms, Dunraven Place (JDW)

Maesteg	❯	Maesteg Bus Station

Porthcawl	❯	Griffin Park John Street Rest Bay Car Park High Tide Inn, Mackworth Road

CAERPHILLY

Bargoed		Bus Terminus, Hanbury Square
Blackwood		Bus Station (Daytime, Mon-Sat) The Sirhowy, High Street (JDW)
Caerphilly		Bus/Railway Terminus (8.00-19.30) Lower Twyn, Tourist Inf. Office (8.00-19.30)
Crosskeys		Sirhowy Valley Country Park
Deri		Parc Cwm Darren (2) (April-Oct)
Nelson		Bus Station
Newbridge		High Street
Oakdale		Pen Y Fan Pond Country Park (April-Oct)
Risca		Tredegar Street

CAERPHILLY
CAERFFILI

Working Together for
the good of all

Caerphilly County Borough Council is committed to providing access to all its services for people with disabilities.

The council incorporates the National RADAR key scheme in various public conveniences throughout the county borough.

For further information please call
01443 873727

Ystrad Mynach ❯ Bedlwyn Road, by Bus Terminus

CARDIFF

Canton ❯ Delta Street
Pontcanna Caravan Site (Site users)
Sophia Gardens Car Park (9.00-16.00)

Cardiff City Centre ❯ Frederick Street
The Hayes
Britannia Park (Daytime) (Port Authority)
Havannah Street (Daytime) (Port Authority)
Capitol Shopping Centre (Private)
Queens Arcade Shopping Centre (Private)
St Davids Shopping Centre (Private)
St Davids 2 Development [Planned] (CP)
Debenhams Store, St Davids Way (Debenhams)
Cardiff Central Station, Subway (Arriva Wales)
Queen Street Station, Platform 1 (Arriva Wales)
Cayo Arms, Cathedral Road (Private)
Crockerton, Greyfriars Road (JDW)
Dewi's, Mary Ann Street (Private)
Edwards, St Marys Street (M&B)
Gatekeeper, Westgate Street (JDW)
Great Western, St Mary Street (JDW)
Ha! Ha! Bar, Greyfriars Road (Private)
The Halfway, Cathedral Road (Private)
Ivor Davis, Cowbridge Road East (JDW)
Jongleurs, Millennium Plaza (Private)
Moloko, Mill Lane (Private)
Nandos, Bute Street, Mermaid Quay (Nandos)
Nandos, St Davids Centre (Nandos)
Nandos, St Marys Street (Nandos)
Old Orleans, Atlantic Wharf (Private)
Old Orleans, Church Street (Private)
O'Neills, St Marys Street (M&B)
Philharmonic, St Marys Street (Prvate)
Prince of Wales, St Mary Street (JDW)
Que Pasa, Trinity St (Marstons)
Robins Bar, Cowbridge Road East (Private)
Varsity, Greyfriars Road (Barracuda)
Walkabout, St Marys Street (Private)
Yates's Bar, Westgate Street (Yates)
Gala Bingo, Batchelor Road (Gala)
Millennium Stadium (Match & Event Days) (Private)

St David's Hall (Hall hrs) (Private)
SWALEC Stadium (Glamorgan Cricket)
National Assembly for Wales (CP)

Cathays ❯ Whitchurch Road, by Library (Park hrs)

Lisvane ❯ Cefn-on-Park, Cherry Orchard Rd (Park hrs)
LlandaffLlandaff Fields, Cathedral Road

Llanishen ❯ Ty Glas Road

Plasnewydd ❯ Albany Road
Roath Park, Boatstage (Park hrs)
Roath Park, Rose Gardens (Park hrs)
Central Bar, Windsor Place (JDW)
Ernest Willows, City Road (JDW)

Rhiwbina ❯ Heol y Deri

Thompson Park ❯ Romilly Road (Park hrs)

Victoria Park ❯ Cowbridge Road East (Park hrs)
Victoria Park, Paddling Pool (Park hrs)
Western Cemetery (Cemetery hrs)

Whitchurch ❯ Penlline Road

MERTHYR TYDFIL

Dowlais ❯ Dowlais Shopping Centre (M&F) (9.00-17.00)

Merthyr Tydfil ❯ Bus Station (9.00-18.00)
Cyfarthfa Park (Park hrs)
by Shopmobility, behind Police Station
St Tydfils Square (9.00-18.00) (Private)
Nandos, Rhydycar Leisure Complex (Nandos)
Y Dic Penderyn, High Street (JDW)

MONMOUTHSHIRE

Abergavenny ❯ Castle Street Car Park
Market Street
Old Bus Station Car Park
Whitehorse Lane
Coliseum, Lion Street (JDW)

		Pandy Caravan Club Site (Caravan Club)
Caldicot	❯	Caldicot Castle Country Park
Chepstow	❯	Bank Street Bridge Street Car Park Bulwark, by Severn Bridge Social Club Riverside
Gilwern	❯	Abergavenny Road
Grosmont	❯	Village Square
Llanthony	❯	Llanthony Abbey Picnic Site Llanthony Priory Car Park (Brecon Beacons NP)
Mitchell Troy	❯	Picnic Site, A449 Northbound
Monmouth	❯	Cattle Market King's Head, Agincourt Square (JDW)
Raglan	❯	Castle Street
Tintern	❯	Beaufort Cottage, The Abbey
Usk	❯	Maryport Street Car Park The Island Usk Picnic Site, A472

NEATH PORT TALBOT

Aberdulais	❯	Aberdulais Falls (National Trust)
Briton Ferry	❯	Lodge Court
Dyffryn Cellwen	❯	Main Road
Neath	❯	Market Victoria Gardens Neath Station, Platform 1 (Arriva Wales) David Protheroe, Windsor Road (JDW)
Pontardawe	❯	Herbert Street Car Park
Port Talbot	❯	Bus Station Princess Margaret Way, Sandfields

Western Avenue, Sandfields
Port Talbot Parkway Station (Arriva Wales)
Lord Caradoc, Station Road (JDW)

Resolven ❯ Canal Car Park

Skewen ❯ Queens Road

NEWPORT

Bettws ❯ Bettws Shopping Centre

Caerleon ❯ Cricket Pavilion, The Broadway (Daytime)
High Street (Daytime)

Maindee ❯ Chepstow Road, opp Police Station (Daytime)

Newport ❯ Bus Station, nr. Corn Street
Caerleon Road, by "Victoria" (Daytime)
Cardiff Road, opp Police Station
Corporation Road, entrance to park (Daytime)
John Frost Sq, by steps to Bus Station
(Mon-Sat 8.00-18.00)
Newport Provision Market (Market hrs)
Kingsway Shopping Centre (Private)
Newport Station, Platform 1/2 (Arriva Wales)
Godfrey Morgan, Chepstow Road (JDW)
Tom Toya Lewis, Commercial Street (JDW)
John Wallace Linton, Cambrian Centre (JDW)
Walkabout, Bridge Street (Private)
Tredegar House Caravan Club Site
(Caravan Club)

RHONDDA CYNON TAF

Aberaman ❯ Cardiff Road

Aberdare ❯ Bus Station, Duke Street
Monk Street
Yr Iuean Ap Iago, High Street (JDW)

Cwmaman ❯ Alexandra Terrace

Maerdy ❯ Maerdy Park

Mountain Ash	❯	Oxford Street
Nantgarw	❯	Nandos, Treforest Ind. Eastate (Nandos)
Pentre	❯	Bridgend Square
Pontyclun M4	❯	Cardiff West Services, J33 M4 (Moto)
Pontypridd	❯	Bus Station, Morgan Street Sardis Road Pontypridd Station, Platform 1 (Arriva Wales) Tumble Inn, Broadway (JDW)
Porth	❯	Hannah Street
Talbot Green	❯	Bus Depot, Talbot Road
Tonypandy	❯	Dunraven Street
Treherbert	❯	Bute Street
Treorchy	❯	nr. Parc & Dare Theatre, Station Road
Ynsybwl	❯	Windsor Place

SWANSEA

Blackpill	❯	Blackpill Lido, off Mumbles Road
Bracelet Bay	❯	Car Park
Caswell Bay	❯	off Caswell Road, Car Park
Clydach	❯	Mond Square, High Street
Gorseinon	❯	West Street, by Bus Station
Gowerton	❯	Gowerton Caravan Club Site (Caravan Club)
Horton	❯	Car Park
Llansamlet	❯	Dylan Thomas, Samlet Road (Private)
Morriston	❯	Woodfield Street, nr, Church

Oxwich	❯	Oxwich Castle (CADW)
Mumbles	❯	Oystermouth Square
Penllegaer M4	❯	Swansea Services, M4 Junct 47 (Moto)
Pontardulais	❯	Water Street
Port Eynon	❯	Foreshore Car Park
Rhossili	❯	nr. Hotel
Swansea	❯	Caer Street, off Princess Way

Civic Centre, Oystermouth Road (Office hrs) CP
Guildhall, Guildhall Road South (Office hrs)
Liberty Stadium (Match Days)
Marina, Maritime Quarter
Marina, Trawler Road
Quadrant Bus Station [Closed at present]
Welcome Lane, off Castle Street
Quandrant Shopping Centre, 1st Floor (Private)
Debenhams Store, The Quadrant (Debenhams)
Swansea Station, Platform 4 (Arriva Wales)
Bank Statement, Wind Street (JDW)
Nandos, Wind Street (Nandos)
Potters Wheel, Kingsway (JDW)
Square, Wind Street (Private)
Varsity, Wind Street/Castle Square (Barracuda)
Walkabout, Castle Square (Private)
Yates's Bar, Caer Street (Yates)

TORFAEN

Cwmbran	❯	John Fielding, Caradoc Road (JDW)
Pontypool	❯	Indoor Market (Market hrs)

John Capel Hanbury, Osborne Rd (JDW)

VALE OF GLAMORGAN

Barry	❯	Court Road/Holton Road MSCP

Knap Car Terrace, Bron y Mor
Park Crescent, Romilly Road
Porthkerry Country Park, Café Car Park
Weston Square, Vere St/Gladstone Rd

Netto Store, Thomson Street (Netto)
Sir Samuel Romilly, Romilly Building (JDW)

Barry Island 〉 Barry Island Car Park, Clive Road
Western Shelter, Paget Road

Cowbridge 〉 Town Hall Car Park, High Street

Llantwit Major 〉 Boverton Rd, Pound Field Shopping Centre
Cwm Colhuw, Llantwit Major Beach
Town Hall Car Park, The Square

Ogmore by Sea 〉 Car Park, off Main Road

Penarth 〉 Albert Road/West Terrace
Cosmeston Village, Lavernock Road
The Esplanade, Italian Gardens
The Esplanade, Penarth Pier
Bears Head, Windsor Road (JDW)

Southerndown 〉 Dunraven Beach opp. car park

NORTHERN IRELAND

ANTRIM

Antrim ⟩ Castle Centre Car Park
Antrim Bus Station (Translink)
Antrim Station (Translink)
Antrim Campus (Northern Regional College))

Crumlin Glen ⟩ Car Park, by bridge

ARDS

Ballyhalbert ⟩ Harbour Road, Car Park

Ballywalter ⟩ Springvale Road, by Tennis Courts

Comber ⟩ Castle Street Car Park
Islandhill Picnic Area, Ringhaddy Road

Cloughey ⟩ Main Road Car Park

Donaghadee ⟩ The Commons, Millisle Road
The Parade (8.00-18.00, later in Summer)

Killinchy ⟩ Whiterock Picnic Area, Ballydorn Road

Millisle ⟩ Ballywalter Road Car Park

Newtownards ⟩ Mill Street
Newtownards Bus Station (Translink)
Spirit Merchant, Regent Street (JDW)

Portaferry ⟩ Castle Park, Exploris

Portavogie ⟩ Anchor Car Park, Springvale Road

ARMAGH

Armagh ⟩ Armagh Bus Station (Translink)

Markethill ⟩ The Square

Tandragee ⟩ Market Street

BALLYMENA

Ballymena

Ballymena Bus/Rail Station (Translink)
CAFÉ Lamont (Northern Regional College)
Farm Lodge Buildings (Northern Regional College)
Trostan Ave. Buildings (Northern Regional College)
Spinning Mill, Broughshane Street (JDW)

BANBRIDGE

Banbridge

Corbet Lough, Aughnacloy Road
Kenlis Street
New Cemetery, Newry Road

Dromore

Dromore Park, Banbridge Road
Market Square

Katesbridge

Katesbridge Picnic Area

Loughbrickland

Village Park, Poynzpass Road

Scarva

Main Str

BELFAST

Central Belfast ⊗ Arthur Lane, Arthur Street (Daytime)
Bankmore Square, Dublin Road
Botanic Gardens (Park hrs)
Church Lane, Ann Street (Daytime)
Custom House Square
Lombard Street
St Georges Market (Market hours)
Winetavern Street (Daytime)
Europa Buscentre (Translink)
Laganside Buscentre (Translink)
Belfast Botanic Station (Translink)
Central Station (Translink)
Great Victoria Street Station (Translink)
Debenhams Store, Castle Court (Debenhams)
Bridge House, Bedford Street (JDW)
Nandos, Bedford Street (Nandos)
Nandos, Victoria Street (Nandos)

East Belfast ⊗ Connswater, Westminster Ave (Mon-Sat, Daytime)
Clara Street (Mon-Sat, Daytime)

North Belfast ⊗ Agnes Street (Mon-Sat, Daytime)
Waterworks, Antrim Road
Yorkgate Station (Translink)

South Belfast ⊗ Cranmore Park, Lisburn Road (Park Hrs)
Drumglass Park, Lisburn Road (Daytime)
Gasworks, Ormeau Road
Ormeau Embankment, Ormeau Bridge (Daytime)
Roselawn Cemetery (Cemetery hrs)
Sir Thomas & Lady Dixon Park (Park hrs)
Stormont Estate (Park hrs)

West Belfast ⊗ Bowling Paviliion, Falls Road (Mon-Fri, Daytime)

CARRICKFERGUS

Carrickfergus ⊗ Harbour Car Park, by Castle
Carrickfergus Station (Translink)
Central Bar, High Street (JDW)

Whitehead ⊗ Whitehead Car Park
Whitehead Station (Translink)

COLERAINE

Castlerock ➤ Promenade (May-Sept)
Hezlett House (National Trust)

Coleraine ➤ Long Commons
Park Street
Railway Road, Leisure Centre Car Park
Strand Road
Coleraine Bus/Rail Station (Translink)
Old Court House, Castlerock Road (JDW)

Downhill ➤ Downhill Beach Car Park (May-Sept)

Garvagh ➤ Bridge Street

Kilrea ➤ Garvagh Road

Portballintrae ➤ Beach Road Car Park
The Harbour (May-Sept)

Portrush ➤ Arcadia (May-Sept)
Dunluce Avenue

Kerr Street
Strand Road, Riverside Park
Whiterocks Car Park (May-Sept)

Portstewart ➤ Harbour Road
Town Hall

COOKSTOWN

Cookstown ➤ Burn Road
Bus Station (Translink)

CRAIGAVON

Lurgan ➤ Castle Lane

Portadown ➤ William Street (Portadown 2000)
Portadown Station (Translink)

DERRY

Derry ◉ Victoria Car Park, Strand Road
Derry City Bus Station (Translink)
Londonderry Station (Translink)
Debenhams Store, Foyleside (Debenhams)
Sainsbury's Store, Strand Road (Sainsbury)
The Diamond, Diamond (JDW)
Ice Wharf, Strand Road (JDW)

DOWN

Ardglass ◉ The Harbour

Ballyhornan ◉ -

Ballynahinch ◉ Windmill Street

Castlewellan ◉ Upper Square

Crossgar ◉ Killyleagh Street

Downpatrick	❯	Market Street Downpatrick Bus Station (Translink)
Killyleagh	❯	Delamont Country Park (Park hrs) High Street
Newcastle	❯	Castle Park Central Promenade Donard Park Downs Road Islands Park South Promenade Bus Station (Translink)
Quoile	❯	Car Park
Saintfield	❯	New Line

DUNGANNON & SOUTH TYRONE

Augher	❯	Clogher Road
Ballygawley	❯	Church Street
Coalisland	❯	Lineside
Dungannon	❯	Scotch Street Dungannon Bus Station (Translink)
Fivemiletown	❯	Main Street
Moy	❯	Charlemont Street
Peatlands Park	❯	Visitor Centre (Natural Heritage)

FERMANAGH

| Enniskillen | ❯ | Enniskillen Bus Station (Translink)
Linen Hall, Townhall Street (JDW) |

LARNE

| Larne | ❯ | Larne Bus Station (Translink)
Larne Station (Translink) |

LIMAVADY

Benone  Beach

Dungiven Main Street

Limavady Catherine Street
Main Street
Bus Station (Translink)

Roe Valley Country Park Dogleap Centre (Natural Heritage)

LISBURN

Hillsborough Ballynahinch Street

Lisburn Civic Centre, Lagan Valley Island (CP)
Lisburn Bus Station (Translink)
Lisburn Station (Translink)
Tuesday Bell. Lisburn Square (JDW)

BOROUGH COUNCIL
LIMAVADY
Comhairle Bhuirg
Léim an Mhadaidh

**Limavady Borough Council
provides access for and awareness
of people with disabilties throughout
all its premises, and incorporates
the National RADAR Key Scheme
in various public conveniences
throughout the Borough**

For further information please contact:
Limavardy Borough Council
7 Connell Street, Limavady
Northern Ireland BT49 0HA
T. 028 777 60305   F. 028 777 29005
www.limavady.gov.uk

**MOYLE
DISTRICT
COUNCIL**

We are delighted to say that all our
disabled toilets within the **Moyle
District Council** area are fitted with
the **RADAR** lock and we are proud to
be a member of the association.

MAGHERAFELT

| Draperstown | Derrynoid Road |
| Magherafelt | Magherafelt Bus Station (Translink) Magherafelt Campus (Northern Regional College) |

MOYLE

Armoy	Main Street
Ballintoy	Harbour
Ballycastle	Harbour Car Park Quay Road Pavilion Seafront Centre
Bushmills	Dundrave Giants Causeway Visitor Centre
Cushendall	Legg Green Mill Street Car Park Waterford Slipway
Cushendun	Beach Car Park
Dunservick	Harbour
Rathlin Island	Church Bay
Waterfoot	Main Street

NEWRY & MOURNE

Annalong	Marine Park (Daytime)
Bessbrook	Fountain Street (Daytime)
Bloodybridge	Amenity Area (Daytime)
Crossmaglen	Loughross Amenity Area (April-Oct) The Square (Daytime)
Hilltown	Rostrevor Road (Daytime)

Kilkeel		Spelga Amenity Area (Apr-Oct, Daytime) Bridge Street (Daytime) Cranfield Beach (M&F) (April-Oct, daytime)
Newry		Marcus Square (Daytime) Newry Sports Centre, Patrick's St (Centre hrs) Newry Town Hall, Bank Parade Bus Station (Translink) Newry Station (Translink)
Rostrevor		The Square (8.00-18.00)
Warrenpoint		The Park, Queen Street (M&F) (Daytime) The Square (Daytime)

NEWTOWNABBEY

Ballyclare		Main Street (7.30-dusk) Sixmilewater River Park (8.00-dusk) Ballyclare Bus Station (Translink)
Jordanstown		Loughshore Park, Shore Road (8.00-dusk)

Newtownabbey 〉 Newtownabbey Bus Station (Translink)

Whiteabbey 〉 Hazelbank Park, Shore Road (8.00-dusk)

NORTH DOWN

Bangor 〉 Abbey Street Car Park, opp. Bus Station
Ballyholme Park, Ballyholme Esplanade
Banks Lane Car Park, Groomsport Road
McKee Clock, Quay Street
Pickie Fun Park, Marine Gardens
Ward Park, Park Drive
Bangor Bus /Rail Station (Translink)

Crawfordsburn Beach 〉 (Natural Heritage)

Car Par 〉 Helens Bay Car Park (Natural Heritage)

Groomsport 〉 Harbour Road

Holywood 〉 Hibernia Street
Seapark Recreation Area

OMAGH

Omagh 〉 Johnston Park/Kevlin Avenue
Scarff's Entry (Daytime)

STRABANE

Castlederg 〉 William Street

Cranagh 〉 Glenelly Road

Donemana 〉 Berryhill Road

Newtownstewart 〉 Main Street

Plumbridge 〉 Fair Green

Sion Mills 〉 Melmount Road

Strabane 〉 Market Street
Dock Street
Strabane Bus Station (Translink)

CHANNEL ISLANDS

GUERNSEY

Castel ❯ Grande Rocque Beach
Saumarez Park
Vazon Beach

St Martins ❯ Icart
Jerbourg Car Park
Moulin Huet Bay Car Park

St Peter Port ❯ Bus Terminus
Castle Emplacement
Crown Pier
North Beach Car Park
St Julians Avenue
White Rock Ferry Terminal

St Peters ❯ L'Erée Beach

St Sampson's ❯ Delancy Park
South Side

Vale ❯ Bordeaux Beach
Chouet Beach
North Side, The Bridge

JERSEY

Grouville ❯ Gorey Common
La Rocque (M&F)

St Brelades ❯ Corbiere
Le Haule
La Pulante
Red Houses
St Aubins
Underground, St Brelades Bay
Woodford, St Brelades Bay

St Clements ❯ La Mare (M&F)
Millards Corner (M&F)

St Helier ❯ First Tower

Liberation Bus Station
Minden Place, Car Park
Patriotic Street, Car Park
Sand Street Car Park
Snow Hill Car Park (M&F) {under review}

St John ❯ Bonne Nuit

St Lawrence ❯ Bel Royal
Millbrook, Promenade
Millbrook, Coromation Park (Park hrs)

St Martin ❯ Archirondel
Gorey House
St Catherines

St Ouens ❯ Greve De Lecq
Le Braye
Les Laveurs

St Peters ❯ Beaumont, Gunsite

Trinity ❯ Rozel

ISLE OF MAN

Douglas   ❯
Drumgold Street Car Park
Jubilee Clock, Loch Promenade
Loch Promenade Gardens
Nobles Park, St Ninian Road
Shaw Brow Car Park, Barrack St
York Road
Colours, Central Promenade (Private)
Fiesta Havana, Wellington Street (Private)

Laxey   ❯
The Harbour

Onchan   ❯
Port Jack
Onchan Pleasure Park (Private)

Peel   ❯
Market Place
Shore Road/Victoria Road
Peel Camp Site (Private)

Ramsey   ❯
Bowring Road
Coronation Park
Market Place
Mooragh Park, Lakeside Pavilion
Ramsey Town Library (Library hrs)

Index of Advertisers

Index

Index

Index

Index

Index

Index

Index

Index

H

Index

Index

Index

Index

Index

Index

Index

Index

Index

Index

Index

Index

Index

Index